The UNCERTAINTY PRINCIPLE

The UNCERTAINTY PRINCIPLE

Essays on Infertility, Conception, Birth, and Quantum Mechanics

JOEL WACHMAN

Alternating Current Press
Boulder, Colorado

The Uncertainty Principle: Essays on Infertility, Conception, Birth, and Quantum Mechanics
Joel Wachman
©2021 Alternating Current Press

Alternating Current
Boulder, Colorado
alternatingcurrentarts.com

ISBN: 978-1-946580-23-8
First Edition: August 2021

For
L. A. S.

The particles are broken; the waves are translucent, laving, roiling with beauty like sharks. The present is the wave that explodes over my head, flinging the air with particles at the height of its breathless unroll; it is the live water and light that bears from undisclosed sources the freshest news, renewed and renewing, world without end.

—Annie Dillard, *A Pilgrim at Tinker Creek*

Thus, I stand naked, with nothing
Except a fierce hunger to fathom this world,
To embark on this road
Without length without breadth.

—Alan Lightman, *Song of Two Worlds*

TABLE OF CONTENTS

The UNCERTAINTY PRINCIPLE

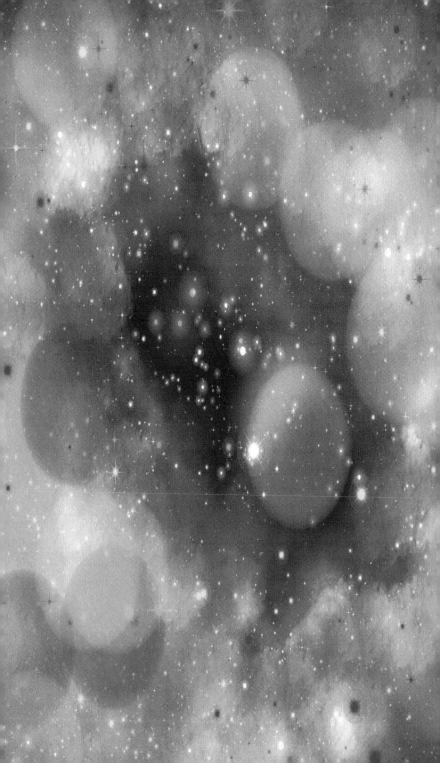

WHAT LITTLE BOYS ARE MADE OF

You marvel that this matter, shuffled pell-mell at the whim of Chance, could have made a man, seeing that so much was needed for the construction of his being. But you must realize that a hundred million times this matter, on the way to human shape, has been stopped to form now a stone, now lead, now coral, now a flower, now a comet; and all because of more or fewer elements that were or were not necessary for designing a man. Little wonder if, within an infinite quantity of matter that ceaselessly changes and stirs, the few animals, vegetables, and minerals we see should happen to be made; no more wonder than getting a royal pair in a hundred casts of the dice. Indeed, it is equally impossible for all this stirring not to lead to something, and yet this something will always be wondered at by some blockhead who will never realize how small a change would have made it into something else.

—Cyrano de Bergerac, *A Voyage to the Moon*

HOW MIRACULOUS THAT YOU ARE YOU! The chromosomes that met in your mother's womb twisted and danced, gyrated and gamboled, knitting the finest threads of protein into every hard and soft structure, the meats and sauces that make up your body. They continued to do so after you were born, while you drooled and cried and shat yourself in your crib, while you learned to speak and walk, became a curious shin-biter, a precarious toddler. Your genes determined the color of your skin, the length of your fingers, the timing of biological milestones like when you would lose your baby teeth. We gave you raw materials: macaroni and cheese, chocolate milk, carrots. The twisted scroll of ancient instructions built your body and your brain, and then, one stupendous day, you became aware. So here you sit, book in hand, a comprehending child made from pieces of earth.

If anything had been different, you, yourself, would be different. You would see the world another way. Suppose your hair had been dark instead of light. Or your eyes green instead of blue. Your sight would have been the same, but would anyone have sung to you, "Oh, where have you been, my blue-eyed son," from "A Hard Rain's a-Gonna Fall"? In your room, you rigged up a guitar, harmonica, and wire hanger to sing Dylan's poetic masterpiece, your innocence protecting you from the tragic message of the song.

A green-eyed person is less susceptible to the sun, so we would have encouraged you more to stay outdoors. You might have become an athlete and, on warm summer afternoons, played basketball with the neighborhood kids instead of looking through your microscope alone in your darkened bedroom. So many small things at the beginning of life are the progenitors of your destiny.

Let us unwind you back into the womb, deconstruct you to a fetus, an embryo, and finally, a blastocyst consisting of only a few hundred cells. On an ultrasound, you appeared as a bright galaxy floating in a starlit field. Just a dozen weeks earlier, your mother lay on her back on an examination table, her shirt pulled up, her lower half sticking to crepe paper. A young woman, a stranger, placed a catheter inside her with empathetic gentleness and sent my sperm on a journey to meet your mother's egg. I did not witness what happened when they met. Now, knowing you so many years later, I can only imagine that the angels sang.

There are a million reasons why life should not come about. Yet, every inch of the earth is smothered in it. In forests and fields and oceans, of course, but also in the most extreme of places. Insects burrow in the desolate sand pits of the American Southwest and the Australian Outback. Translucent brine shrimp in boiling geysers a thousand feet under the ocean's surface frolic and fornicate with abandon. Every one of these creatures begins as a pair of DNA molecules that dance to a microscopic Lambada. Yet, the one single event among these billions that really counts is the one that made you. Where did you come from, that you sit here comfortably reading? Seven years ago, you did not exist. And now here you are, *sui generis*, the result of a simple pairing in your mother's womb.

If all this talk of parental anatomy makes you uncomfortable, imagine it happening to another person, or to your cat, Erwin. And while you're at it, feel free to give names to the sperm and egg—Sherman and Ethel—to make them more approachable, to quell your embarrassment of talking about sexual things. Watching Sherman the sperm dash toward Ethel, one might think he was a cell with a mission. In fact, sperm are highly specialized cells. They have only one reason to exist. They have a head to carry genetic material, a body that carries enzymes for softening up Ethel's shell, and, of course, that famous tail, which propels them diligently forward and upward on a three-inch voyage to the blessed event. Sherman measures only one six-hundredths of an inch long, so this last stretch is the equivalent of a person swimming two miles. Ethel has already done her work —she popped out of her ovary and drifted for a day. Now she waits passively, hoping somebody—anybody —comes to call before she tumbles too far and it is too late. The moment arrives. Athletic Sherman pushes ahead of the rest and nuzzles his head beneath her surface. Until that moment, Ethel was available to anyone who would have her, but now she becomes faithful to him alone, the one who made it through.

Before cellular replication can begin, Sherman has to release his DNA inside of Ethel (it seems there is no avoiding charged language after all). His chromosomes join with hers, linking up molecule by molecule. If everything goes exactly right, proteins will begin to form. The proteins link and stack, becoming a cell wall, some mitochondria, and organelles with horror-movie-like names: the endoplasmic reticulum, the Golgi apparatus. After a while, Ethel develops bulges. A new cell wall creeps down her middle. She loses her svelte ovoid shape as her two sides grow bigger and her middle grows narrower. Ethel is a zygote now. In a matter of hours, she will split into two identical daughter cells. Each of those cells will divide and split again. One becomes two. Two becomes four, then eight, then sixteen, then thirty-two, and so on, until there emerges a little ball of human flesh: an embryo.

Anyone building a new body inside her own needs to eat the ingredients that babies are made of. Your mother is fond of saying you were made out of pizza and chocolate. When she got pregnant, I assumed she would soon be sending me out on impossible midnight forays for Cherry Garcia ice cream, General Gau's chicken, iced decaf soy vanilla lattés, or dill pickles, that ultimate cliché. But she spared me that. Once, after all the stores had closed and our freezer was empty and it was going to be impossible to slake her desires, she did turn to me in her sleep and say, "Mmmm . . . pepperoni." My eyes popped open, my fingers gripped the mattress in anticipation, but she rolled over, emitted a half-hearted burp, and went back to sleep. The recipe for a baby boils down to a few simple elements. Take the water out of our bodies, and what's left are the dry goods, just enough to fill the sand pail you bring to the beach. Carbon, sodium, potassium, a dash of zinc, maybe, and a few others. In short, we are made of the same stuff as everything else under the sun. When the Bible says man is made of the earth and that we will return to the earth, it can be taken at face value. However, this is a scientific discussion, not a theological one. I wish to shine some light on the phenomena that made your body grow from a single cell into a person who can read about it.

A high-school sex-ed teacher would say that the male seed fertilizes the female egg, and then a fetus begins to grow. But then, sex-ed teachers are paid to gloss over relevant details. With more rigor, we might approach the issue as a professional biologist would, saying that a sperm and an egg join, and the combined system undergoes a process of mitosis, producing a blastocyst that implants some time later on the uterine wall. A biochemist would say that the deoxyribonucleic acid undergoes a polymerase reaction in the presence of a catalyst. We can go on and on, zooming inward and downward to reveal more details, using language that becomes more arcane at each order of magnitude. At some point, we will find ourselves inside the very atoms themselves, caught inside a storm of electromagnetic forces, a hail of characters with names straight out of the Bionicles—Bosons, Leptons, and Quarks. Perhaps there, among the smallest of possible objects, between the invisible in-betweens, we will discover the secret that makes you you.

If you are the kind of person who wants to know how atoms are shaped (and I know you are), you might think of them as tiny malted milk balls: a bunch of electrons encircling a crunchy center of protons and neutrons. All of the matter you will encounter in your life, everything you will touch or smell or taste, is made of atoms. That is what makes them so important. It is good and right and very scientific to ask what those electrons and protons are made from. The answer is tricky. Saying one kind of matter is made of a second kind is a sure way to get caught in a vicious circle, a never-ending loop of questions leading to more questions.

The search for the smallest pieces of matter soon leads to a point where it is impossible to distinguish matter from energy. When physicists measure an atom's constituent parts, they find that they do not have mass in the conventional sense. We measure the size of an electron, for example, in electron volts, which is a unit of energy. When an electron loses energy, it spits out a photon in the form of light or radio waves. Subatomic particles, mere wisps, no heavier than a thought, are responsible for the forces that hold an atom's nucleus together, and for electric charge and magnetic attraction. It would seem, then, that the closer we look, the more it appears that the world is not really made of *stuff* at all. At the smallest level, it is made of *influences*.

There is something else very strange and special about subatomic particles. It is useful to think of an electron as a tiny billiard ball that whizzes around the atomic environment. As it hovers and spins, shimmers and shimmies around the center of an atom, the electron will change its orbit, sometimes sticking close to the nucleus, sometimes wandering far enough that it encounters other electrons on other atoms. The strange and special thing is that an electron appears to travel from a low orbit to a high orbit instantly, in a single jump. The distance that it jumps corresponds to the energy it gains or loses, which comes in discrete, predictable amounts. When the electron has less energy, it takes a low orbit around the nucleus. When it gets more energy, it jumps to one of a few predetermined higher orbits. It disappears from one place and reappears in the other in the same instant. This is certainly different from the behavior of a spacecraft that finds a new orbit around a moon or planet. When the spacecraft climbs from the troposphere (where airplanes fly) to the thermosphere (to visit the International Space Station), a spaceship visits every place in between. An electron, on the other hand, does not have to visit every place between close-to-the-nucleus and far-from-the-nucleus. In an atom, an electron gains and loses energy in discrete packets. Physicist Albert Einstein called this a *quantum* transition, as opposed to a gradual one. All subatomic particles display this sort of behavior. Atom- and molecule-sized pieces of matter do, too. But somewhere between the scale of the ultramicroscopic and the visible, quantum effects disappear. That is fortunate, because it would be very inconvenient, indeed, if objects like spaceships, automobiles, or nicely browned slices of toast were to pop out of existence in one place, only to reappear in another.

Falling in love with your mother was a quantum transition. One moment I was a lonely, miserable sod plodding close to the ground; the next moment I was carried aloft in fresh air. I never experienced a moment of being in-between. And when, a few years later, you were conceived under the fluorescent light of a clinic examination room, my body became entangled with yours in the way that particles do. Wheresoever you go, so goes a part of me.

We almost didn't meet, your mother and I. My bags were packed, and my pocket held a one-way ticket to Paris, and then she showed up at my farewell party, a friend of one of my friends. She was striking: even her most casual movements were efficient and intelligent. I was entranced by the wit and spark of her conversation. A few hours earlier, I had been keen on my new life. I was anticipating independence and sweet liberation after years of study and work. Her appearance was an alarming shard of light and heat. The tenor of my departure changed. When I got on the plane the next day, I was encumbered by the tug of regret for something important I had left behind. Six months later, I saw her in a Paris bakery, buying a raspberry tart. She was passing through my adopted city and just happened to find herself on my street at the moment I was walking past. If we had been lazy or fatalistic, we would have exchanged a nervous chuckle, shared a polite moment, and moved on. But your mother was a romantic, and I was eager to show her my adopted city. Soon we were walking along the quays of the river, hand-in-hand, talking about the love story of Édouard Manet and Berthe Morisot, the relative funniness of Catskill Comics, and the best *pâtisseries* within walking distance of my apartment. After she left, I started receiving handmade postcards and elaborate gifts of music and art. Our love reached across the Atlantic, traveling by post, by satellite, cable, and ship, until one day your mother appeared on my doorstep carrying nothing more than a book and a passport.

We could have chosen different people, different paths. We could have been the parents of other children. Looking back, it may appear that we were fated to have you. But fate is only the reinterpretation of past events. In the present moment, you always exercise free will. If your mother and I hadn't rediscovered each other, can we say things would have been the same for you, but for different parents? Or must we admit with cruel precision that you would never have been born?

The biologist Richard Dawkins explains that all life on Earth could have arisen from a single chemical event almost four billion years ago. Perhaps a single strand of rogue proto-DNA replicating in the primordial soup, more like a virus than an actual living thing, was the ancestor of every bacterium, plant and animal, from Tyrannosaurus Rex to garlic, from *E. coli* to Angelina Jolie. The constituent parts of DNA, amino acids, are the natural product of the chemical reactions that would have taken place when the Earth was young and hot.

You can cook some up yourself in a cheap science experiment involving ammonia, water, various salts, and electricity. It is likely that the first cells came about once the amino acids got organized enough to assemble themselves into proteins. That all happened a very, very long time ago—about 3,500,000,000 years before you were born. The proteins piled on top of one another to form a complex self-replicating structure, and for many generations, the seas were peppered with these miniscule motes. First simple ones, then more complex ones that finally looked like cells. You can see their millions-times great-grandchildren today in a drop of pondwater under your microscope, wiggling haplessly, entirely unaware that they are the oldest things on Earth. In theory, you can trace your own ancestry back to those insensate microorganisms by navigating a reverse course through adaptation and mutation. It only takes a tiny change in the DNA of an animal, says Dawkins, to affect very significant visible changes in the species. The most difficult thing, for we who live but a clipped century, is to grasp the idea that evolutionary changes in animals happen over many generations, over hundreds of millennia, and that a small change is magnified when it is part of a long-lived or very complex system. Each mutation that propagates to another generation causes still others, as cause and effect ripple through time.

The guiding principle of classical evolutionary theory is that mutations happen at random. Mutations become permanent features in a species as individuals carrying that mutation reproduce. Naturalist Charles Darwin first noticed this on the Galapagos Islands, where he found several kinds of finches living together. These finches differed mostly in the shapes of their beaks. Some had narrow, sharp beaks suitable for rooting insects out of small places or picking leaves and berries. Others had stubbier beaks that could crack open hard nuts and seeds. In almost every other respect, they looked similar. All of these subspecies could have had a common ancestor, but over time the birds developed these different beaks to reduce competition for food.

The manner in which this came about is a horror story of starvation and infant mortality that goes something like this: In any given generation, some number of finches were born. Some had slightly longer beaks and some slightly stubbier ones. On the finch schoolyard, many young finches vied for a limited number of nuts and crunchy insects. The ones with the shorter, stronger beaks, better suited to opening the harder nuts, were more likely to be well-fed and to survive into adulthood. The ones with longer, narrower beaks were more likely to die of starvation before they could reproduce—unless they could develop a taste for a different kind of food. So, the long-beaked finches wandered about until they came to an area populated with tasty green lettuces and bright berries. Desperate and hungry, they stuffed themselves full of this strange food. In the generations that followed, the children of the Strong Beaks inherited the strong-beak gene and stuck around to enjoy the nuts, while the children of the Long Beaks inherited the long-beak gene and developed a cuisine based on leaves and berries.

The proposition of cascading effects applies to evolution, for sure, but it also happens in individuals. A single synapse firing in your brain might lead you to make a choice: To turn left or right? Eat that cupcake or leave it for later? Reach for a shiny penny on the ground or keep walking? Imagine how any one of these choices can affect your future, your happiness, the kind of adult you become. Could it be that some elements of human thought are set in motion by quantum events?

A synapse fires because of a buildup of electrical charge—an excess of electrons on one side of a gap, a paucity on the other. But sooner or later, upon the arrival of that last electron, the one that breaks the camel's back, so to speak, the reaction is set in motion. The charge is released, the electrons make the leap across the great divide, the signal travels to the next neuron over, completing the thought. You reach down, and grab that penny. But now you can see under the bushes that line the fence to the park. Through the fence you see a man playing the guitar and harmonica. "Come on, Dad." You tug at my hand. We walk around the corner, past a hotdog vendor, through the gates with the gargoyles on top, and into the park. The man with the harmonica and guitar is just around the bend in the path. You run to him and plunk yourself down on a damp rock nearby and listen with rapt attention. The man smiles at you, then at me, from behind his harmonica. He smiles with his eyes. He is playing the folk classic, "A Hard Rain's a-Gonna Fall." It is easy to dismiss these things as a series of random events. But the events are connected. Each event is dependent upon the previous, and one can trace a direct line backward from your harmonica to the penny to the synapse firing in your brain to the arrival of that last electron. From there, they go back to the development of your mind and body, to the doubling of cells in your mother's womb, the penchant for musicality you inherited from your grandfather the concert violinist, from your great-great grandfather the nineteenth-century Lithuanian cantor. In life, there are many paths forward, but only one way back.

There were times in the beginning when your mother and I argued so hard that we almost broke up. Once, she made it all the way into the Métro and was waiting for the next train to the airport. I tumbled down the stairs, shouting out her name, the echoes of my plaintive apologies arousing the curiosity of the two homeless men on a bench, each clutching his own bottle, who jeered at us as if they were watching a boxing match. Had it been an argument over some irreconcilable philosophical or political difference, perhaps I would not have tried so hard to recant. You cannot go on living with someone when your worldviews demonstrate a catastrophic failure to intersect. But our argument was about cheese, of all things, a stupid package of mascarpone, which I insisted was fine, but her super-sensitive nose told her was rancid. I had already whisked some into the eggs and ruined the pie. I remember feeling as if a little part of our relationship died that day. I did not think we would ever recover, either as a couple or as individuals. Ten years later, we are still together, our love deeper than ever, and the episode relegated to the biohazard waste bin of things we never talk about.

Then there was the time I stepped in front of a bus, and your mother saved my life. It was in London, on Piccadilly. We had just come out of a stationery shop where she'd bought me a gift of matching pens. A fountain pen and a ballpoint, sleek and black. (I am using the fountain pen to write this story.) We were about to cross the street to a pub. I don't know why it happened then. I had lived in England for long periods over many decades, driven on country roads and in the city. I had internalized the fact that British automobiles drive on the left. Nevertheless, I stepped into the street with a pointless glance in the wrong direction. I heard her yell and felt her grip my shoulders to pull me back. I looked up in time to see a white-paneled van barreling down on me. I was scarcely back on the curb when it whooshed past. The driver hadn't time to put on the brakes or honk the horn, but I saw the look of surprise frozen on his face. It is an indelible image on my visual cortex, a millisecond extended until it fills a whole minute, like one of those photographs taken with a strobe lamp—a bullet piercing a balloon, a hummingbird's wings paused midstroke. When I realized how close I had come to getting killed, I broke into a sweat and saw stars. Many years later, as Ruby lay on the exam table, her legs in the stirrups, lying still for the recommended ten-minute insemination, I wondered if the reason we were having trouble was that I wasn't supposed to be there at all. I should have died in London five years earlier. My continued presence was an accident that put the universe out of balance. There was one life too many. We would not be allowed to bring another one into existence.

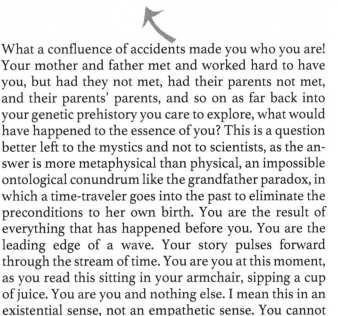

What a confluence of accidents made you who you are! Your mother and father met and worked hard to have you, but had they not met, had their parents not met, and their parents' parents, and so on as far back into your genetic prehistory you care to explore, what would have happened to the essence of you? This is a question better left to the mystics and not to scientists, as the answer is more metaphysical than physical, an impossible ontological conundrum like the grandfather paradox, in which a time-traveler goes into the past to eliminate the preconditions to her own birth. You are the result of everything that has happened before you. You are the leading edge of a wave. Your story pulses forward through the stream of time. You are you at this moment, as you read this sitting in your armchair, sipping a cup of juice. You are you and nothing else. I mean this in an existential sense, not an empathetic sense. You cannot know what it would be like to be the child of different parents, just as I cannot know what it is like to be my own son, a blue-eyed boy. I have been a child, and I have looked up at my parents' loving faces, but I never looked up at my own loving face. I have been rocked to sleep by your mother, but she is not my mother. I can imagine the experience of being blue-eyed, of being colorblind, of having your name. But in all these cases, I would be thinking about me, myself, younger, shorter, standing in your adorable light-up sneakers. My experience is filtered through the fact of my being me, the author of this sentence. The quality of being a specific individual begins in the womb, perhaps before the first moments of cellular division. The curves and workings of your body and mind are set in motion by the random pairing of sperm and egg, by the moment of conception, by your parents' choice of mate, by their parents' choices before them.

Where is that elusive substance of you? In the superstrings that hold together the ten dimensions of the particles of your body. In the quantum jump that caused an electron to bind your mother's DNA to mine. In the contrived meeting of Sherman and Ethel in a hospital room on a sunny day in June. Because a certain couple made a thousand right decisions and ended up together. Because their firing synapses, hormonal juices, and lonely flesh made them ready to love each other. Because of the lives they led until then, and the way they were born and raised, and five hundred generations back to your ancestors Abraham and Sarah, who were subject to the caprices of nature. And back a thousand generations more to the not-too-distant origins of man. Because human life evolved that way. Because conditions on Earth were just right, the necessary chemicals were present in the right concentrations, and the temperature on the newborn planet was not too hot, not too cold. Because Earth was the right distance from the Sun. Because of the laws of celestial mechanics which, in turn, were decreed at the beginning, fourteen billion years ago in the first picosecond, when everything that ever was or ever will be was contained in a singularity the size of two human cells. Look! Look! There you are. Deep inside that quantum spark. How marvelous, you crumb of universe. And there, surrounding you, closer than the smallest grain of space and burning hot as ten trillion suns, there and everywhere is my love for you. It is the size of all known space and time.

THE
SCIENTIFIC
METHOD

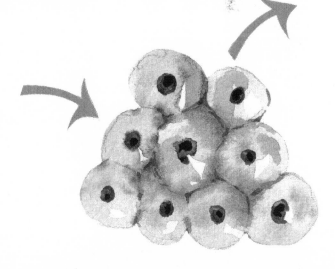

We are faced with a mechanism entirely different from the probabilistic one of physics, and that cannot be reduced to ordinary laws of physics. . . . Living matter, while not eluding the laws of physics . . . is likely to involve laws of physics hitherto unknown.

—Erwin Schrödinger, *What Is Life?*

THE FIRST TIME RUBY AND I HAD SEX WITHOUT BIRTH CONTROL I THOUGHT, THAT'S IT, I'LL BE A FATHER BY NOVEMBER. We went at it with light abandon, and I felt free and vulnerable, more naked than ever, and more in love. I had needed some cajoling to commit to the idea of having a child. I knew I would be a responsible parent, and to me that meant shifting my priorities to place the baby at the nucleus of our family. I feared that Ruby and I would have to give up many things that made us happy in the name of providing a safe and nurturing environment for our child. Then Ruby said, "Look, a baby doesn't have to stop us from having adventures. We're the ones who will set the tone. If it's normal for us, it'll be normal for the baby. I don't have any intention of becoming boring." She helped me to imagine us as a well-managed team, slipping in and out of foreign cities, singing songs on airplanes and long car rides, embracing our child's innocent delight. My relationship with Ruby was nourished by our enjoyment of humor, books, food, friends, and travel. Moreover, when we were with each other, a third persona emerged, an intangible presence that was better than either of us. It was quick, adventurous, and ebullient. But it was illusory. Our child could be the pure and lasting manifestation of our love.

It was with shared optimism we threw Ruby's pills into the trash. Went through one or two passionate months, then life intervened, and we had a dry spell. Then we were back to wanting each other again, groping over the breakfast table, flirting in public, whispering naughty promises to each other at dinner parties. One day, Ruby looked at me with a curious expression and said, "Shouldn't I be pregnant?" So, we started counting. Ruby sat at the table, her head resting on her hand, her hair falling over her face. Out came a pocket calendar I had never seen before, with little red X's on certain days.

"We did it this many times in January, February, skipped March, April—no, only once in April—May, June—here we are in the middle of July. Something should have happened by now."

Conception is an elusive process that takes place on a microscopic scale in an invisible location under circumstances that are not reproducible. Despite this, many people think they'll get pregnant the first time they have sex without protection. It's been hammered into us since we were teenagers. When you're a horny sixteen-year-old with a perfect body and a fresh set of eggs, the chances you'll get knocked up are around sixty percent. Fool around at thirty, and those percentages go way down. At thirty-five or forty, you stand a better chance of winning the church raffle than of conceiving. This is the first disillusionment about conceiving a kid: it might be harder than it seems.

The world we observe with the naked eye, the world described by Aristotle, René Descartes, and Isaac Newton, is made of ideal objects with precise boundaries and states that are easy to recognize. From the four archetypal elements (earth, air, fire, water) to the common states of matter (gas, liquid, solid), we expect nature to give us orderly categorizations and predictable transitions. Our experiences, and therefore our descriptions of the world, are bounded by the limits of our perceptions. Scientific history is the story of reinterpreting subjectivity, and sometimes completely ignoring it in favor of evidence derived from experimentation. Astronomer Nicolaus Copernicus showed that the Earth rotates around the Sun, despite the long-held delusion that we stand on a fixed point in the center of the universe. Biologist and chemist Louis Pasteur showed that diseases can be caused by invisible microorganisms and not by spirits or humors of the spleen. Every significant moment in science opens a fissure between reason and faith. Science takes small steps. Observing. Formalizing a hypothesis. Testing the hypothesis under controlled conditions. Faith is subjective. It requires no proof other than the conviction of the individual. Science follows a logical sequence of assertions and conclusions, such as "A because B, and B because C." Faith stops at "because."

So, how do we accept the revelations of the last century that reveal that matter ultimately has no substance? We are made of flesh; we stand on the ground, feel the weight of our favorite objects in our hands. When we walk barefoot on a tile floor, feel the crack of a fastball against a bat, wiggle sea sand between wet toes, we are intimate with the substance of the earth. Even porous materials are made of molecules and atoms that exert force against our skin. But atoms are made of particle-waves, of stuff that is neither one thing nor the other but both at once. Particles will behave like waves, and waves will behave like particles. They accomplish this by interacting with other particles or by coming in contact with a subatomic force, or even, as theoretical physicist Werner Heisenberg discovered, simply by being observed. How do we conduct ourselves when faced with a world that appears to be made of ghosts?

For Ruby and me, it seemed the best way to conceive was to embrace scientific method. If Ruby's body was not becoming pregnant, the answer must lie somewhere deep inside, in the mushy parts, the mysterious organs and processes that we have heard of but never actually seen. We would give those parts names, for by giving something a name, it becomes knowable. We would dissect them, tag them with brilliant tinctures, so we could compare the defective ones against a control. We would study the processes, the cycles, the biochemical reactions that produce fluids, cramps, and headaches, and relieve them of their mystery. We would scrutinize the genetic software line by line, searching for the plus that should be a minus, or the faulty if/then statement, using the most logical methodologies. Perhaps there was a mistake with the way my sperm were multiplying and dividing. I was never any good at arithmetic. Ruby and I believed we could find the problem under a microscope, and then, with the stroke of a pencil or a change in our habits or even a doctor's prescription, we could change it. If having a child was a matter of bringing the right elements together at the right time under the right conditions, then we would be saved by science. But if that failed, too, then we would know that physicist Erwin Schrödinger was right: the laws that pertain to elementary bodies do not apply to our own.

We started with rhythm. With a bit of help from the Internet and some ovulation test strips, we were able to plot Ruby's menstrual, biorhythmic, and circadian cycles to pinpoint the precise hours during which she would be the most fertile. We agreed to make love at those times, as well as on the days immediately before and after, just to be sure. Scheduling sex down to the precise hour is a turnoff unless you're anticipating a clandestine tryst with a secret lover. In marriage, you already know everything about your partner's day— when she wakes, eats, shits, works, watches television. Of course, I was pleased at the prospect of regular sex— I'm a regular guy. But I hadn't anticipated the degree to which the spontaneity would be eliminated. Everything was to be prescribed, including the very self-conscious way in which we performed the act at a specific moment, in a specific manner: male superior, female prone, with her hips elevated.

Ruby's cycle didn't always cooperate with our busy schedule. Even if she had some advance warning, she still had to reschedule her dentist appointments or cancel an art history class she was teaching. Too often, the peak of her ovulation cycle caught me off guard. I would be at the office, or at the gym, or on my commute into work. One day in September, I was standing in a conference room explaining the details of a computer system I had designed. I'd placed my phone face up on the table. My manager and my staff, about twenty people in all, listened politely while I waved my hands toward the diagrams and figures projected on a screen.

I didn't see the text message come in. My manager did. "Is this urgent?" she asked, handing me the phone.

"Be here now," it read.

Speaking in front of a crowd came easily to me, but now I felt my skin prickle and my heart beat rapidly. If I said it was urgent, my colleagues might think someone was injured or in trouble. If I said it wasn't, then I would have no excuse to leave. There was a convincing argument that, in some way, a life was at stake, and so I stammered, "Yes. No. Nobody's . . . I gotta go." My manager knew that Ruby and I were trying to conceive. It was unavoidable since I had to miss so many mornings and afternoons for appointments at the clinic. As I grabbed my backpack and made for the door, I thought I saw her wink in my direction.

I had given up riding my bicycle to work, but now I regretted it because the taxi got stuck in traffic, subtracting precious minutes from our fertility window. Ruby's text messages went from sexy to demanding. The next one was a selfie with her bare shoulder and a flirtatious smile. "Hurry!" The one after that was a picture of her pouting, with a caption that read: "where are you?"

After fumbling with the lock on the front door, I flew into the house, dropped my backpack and phone, and ran up the steps to our bedroom. Ruby was sitting up in bed wearing a bathrobe and reading a book.

"Hiya," she said.

"Sorry, I was in a meeting," I replied.

She put down the book and snuggled under the covers. "Well, it appears it's time for your performance review."

Ruby had a surprise for me in October. We were at a dinner party with some old friends. She squeezed my hand and left the table. I found her in my friend's upstairs bathroom, leaning against the sink, her underwear hanging from the bathtub spout. In the heat of the moment, we bumped against the sink and knocked the medicine cabinet open by accident. Out came all of the usual things: razors, toothpaste, aspirin. Then a few incriminating items appeared: a pregnancy test, prenatal vitamins, and a small calendar. Next to the printed numbers indicating the days of the month, the telltale countdown. It was comforting to find these artifacts in someone else's house at that particular moment. It made me feel like I was part of a club or a secret society. Rotarians have their breakfasts. Shriners have their parades and silly hats. Couples desperate to conceive keep special calendars and screw in strange places.

Ruby climbed into the bathtub and put her feet up over the edge, assuming an angle that would help the fertile ingredients combine. Her chin was pressed down against her chest and her arms flailed against the porcelain as she tried to get a grip. She slipped downward a few times, then finally grabbed hold of the spigot and found a manageable balance.

"I'm just going to wait a couple of minutes like this," she grunted. "You should go back out. It's not polite for both of us to be gone so long."

I left her crouching half-naked in the tub and closed the door. Inside that sealed room, Ruby may have been conceiving our child. It was impossible to know until she took a pregnancy test. Or unless there were some way of watching what was happening inside of her.

This state of knowing but not knowing reminded me of the thought experiment proposed by Schrödinger that illustrates the uncertainty principle in quantum mechanics. Schrödinger found a way to craft the lesson without arcane equations or theoretical concepts. He turned it into an accessible children's story involving familiar objects (a box), an empathetic character (a cat), and a dramatic ending (the cat lives or dies). This was a genius stroke of science writing that captured the imagination of physicists and lay people, artists, and writers, making it the most famous thought experiment of the twentieth century.

A cat—call him S. Cat—sits in a closed box. I always thought of it as a large shoebox, but it could be any kind of sealed box, as long as there is enough air for the kitty and neither the experimenter nor the cat can see the other. S. Cat is curious about the apparatus the experimenter has put in the box with him—a tiny quantity of radioactive material. A Geiger counter. A Rube-

Goldberg setup connecting the Geiger counter to a hammer poised above a vial of poisonous gas. S. Cat paws at the apparatus, licks himself, then falls asleep in a corner. The experiment begins when the scientist closes the lid. In the hour that follows, there's a fifty/fifty chance that an atom within the radioactive material will decay, emitting a subatomic particle. The particle will fly into the Geiger counter, which will release the hammer, which in turn will smash the vial of poisonous gas, cutting short one of poor S. Cat's nine lives. If the atom does not decay, S. Cat will live to sleep another day.

Schrödinger asks, is S. Cat alive or dead at the end of the hour? Both, he answers. And neither. The uncertainty principle implies that a particle can exist as both wave and particle, and the very act of observing forces it into one state or the other.

Imagine waves spreading out across the surface of a body of water, reflecting the dappled sunlight that issues through the trees along the shore. Your eye catches the effervescent shimmer of a hundred stars among the wave-crests. From your vantage point on the rocky edge where your bare feet are submerged, waves cover the surface in textured patterns of alternating dark and light. Houndstooth and fleurs-de-lys, supple and serrated, wide, flat, and, apparently, stationary. Looking down, you see that the waves are in fact approaching your frozen feet, and as you step further into the water, you see them break against your calf and lose their form. The houndstooth becomes a messy whorl. By stepping into the center of a wave, you have caused the wave to change its state.

Schrödinger leads the reader to come to the absurd conclusion that the cat is also in two states, at once dead and alive, until the particle-wave has been observed. Of course, nothing like this really happens in the world of cats and boxes. The star of this experiment is not S. Cat but the radioactive nucleus, which performs an existential balancing act, remaining both wave and particle until the box is opened. S. Cat is a bridge between the quantum world and the world of familiar sizes.

Schrödinger's *Gedankenexperiment* raises some disturbing philosophical questions for anyone who takes the time to *gedank* about it. If matter can be in a superposition of two states, that means our own bodies' particles are fickle, ambivalent, subject to wavering. Our brains are made of the same basic stuff as all matter, and it is very likely that they are affected by this quantum business. If our thoughts are nothing more than the firing of neurons (and this has yet to be proven, though it seems the most logical explanation), then free will is, to a certain extent, a result of kismet. For that matter, perhaps consciousness itself is what happens when there are quantum fluctuations in a dense neurological environment.

These philosophical implications would be hard to prove. Biochemistry may yield a more concrete example. Quantum mechanics almost certainly plays a role in the chain reactions that occur among the complex proteins and enzymes we are made of. The chemical reactions that occur at the moment of conception, the interplay among the molecules of DNA, are subject to the same caprices, the transcendental behaviors that cause S. Cat to be simultaneously alive and dead.

One branch of science asserts that S. Cat is not in a superposition of states at all. Instead, at the precise moment when the observer opens the box, the universe diverges, creating one universe where the cat is alive, and one where he is not. In one universe, the observer takes the cat home and strokes it lovingly; in the other, he buries it in the backyard. The "many worlds" theory proposes that every possible combination of events can and does occur in some other worlds that are superimposed upon the one that we are accustomed to. Where are these other worlds? They are here and now, but they are in a different here and a different now, like two performances of the same play with the same actors on the same stage. Our familiar world, which is plagued, brutish, and unjust may be just one among many. Perhaps there are an infinite number of worlds. A world where cats are the dominant species, and S. Cat is the one who conducts the experiment. A world in which Schrödinger himself was never born. A world in which we have all achieved enlightenment. A world in which having a child is simply a matter of wanting one.

By November, Ruby still hadn't gotten pregnant, and she was becoming testy. We went on trying to conceive with all the romance of two plumbers plugging a leak. At this point, we started to introduce some not-so-scientific methods into our experiment. In her desperation, Ruby—under normal circumstances a practical person—took to hanging out in the kind of bookstores that hang crystals in the window. She had our astrological charts drawn up. We rearranged the furniture in the bedroom to foster a more fertile *feng shui*. (I told her: if that works it will say a lot for quantum non-determinism. She told me to shut up and rotate the end tables.) We went on a daily regimen of homeopathic pharmacopoeia intended to boost my sperm count and make her uterus as welcoming as a suite at the Ritz. In December, science and mysticism failed equally. It seemed there was nothing we could do to influence what was going on inside her. We began to sleep on opposite sides of the bed.

In January, Ruby's fertile hours peaked on my birthday. Despite the fact that lovemaking is my favorite birthday gift, I was resentful because she said I couldn't drink wine since the alcohol might kill off a few dozen sperm. I complained, implored, and made obtuse claims that I had been on some binges that had killed off a few dozen brain cells, and it hadn't affected my intellect any. "Apparently it has," she retorted. We did it that night female superior, male petulant.

Ruby's obsession with baby-making became pathological. In bed she was single-minded. Having sex had become a means to an end. My body was a mere sperm-bottle, and getting at the contents through sex was a hassle. I had become one of those frustrating blister packs you have to destroy in order to get at the toy or tool behind the plastic. We weren't making love anymore. We weren't even fucking, since fucking involves pleasure. It was January, and lovemaking had waned from a delight to a chore. We were stressed out and disillusioned, and when I reached out to caress her, Ruby flinched. She lay on her back and said, "Just get it over with," which made it impossible for me even to start.

We lay apart from each other for an hour, too agitated to sleep. Silent, sexless, our desiccated organs pale as two beached fish, unable to conjure why we couldn't accomplish a simple thing like conception.

"A friend of mine recommended a doctor," Ruby said, sitting on the side of the bed with her back toward me.

"We don't need any doctors. We just need to keep trying," I replied, with an effort to sound upbeat. I could tell that I was understating the gravity of the situation. It was a familiar feeling that emerges whenever I bump against Ruby's resolve, knowing that she has thought something through more thoroughly than I. There is always some subtle angle that I miss, which makes me feel stupid, or like I've been doped with some drug that makes me logy and aphasic. At this moment, our relationship seemed to hinge on a single blind spot.

There is no point in actually carrying out the Schrödinger's Cat experiment because it is not repeatable. There is nothing you can do that will influence the outcome, so there is nothing you can learn from it. Put another way, Schrödinger's Cat is the best illustration of how effective nature is at concealing the cause of things that are beyond our control. The mechanism of everyday things is governed by an infinite number of variables. Even if we were able to change just the right combination of values—adding a little here, multiplying a little there—they would not be sufficient to push the universe off course. The inertia of destiny is immense.

S. Cat sits in the box. It is dark. He is drowsy. From time to time, he kicks one of his hind legs. Maybe he is dreaming of running through a field of tall grass, hunting a small animal. An atavistic dream, resounding in his psyche millennia after all the hunting instinct has been bred out of his race. His flaccid stumpy body couldn't outrun a parked car. Or maybe he is dreaming of running from the deadly apparatus sealed in the box with him. He is looking for a good place to hide, but he knows—he *knows*—the thing that will kill him is small enough to sneak in anywhere. The sixty seconds tick off so slowly S. Cat begins to think he was born in this box and will probably die there. Or maybe he has already died. Maybe, he thinks (waking up a little now), maybe this box is all there will be from now on. Just darkness and quiet. S. Cat wonders: How is never-ending darkness and quiet when you're alive different from the never-ending darkness and quiet of being dead? Is it because I'm hungry and need to stretch my back that I know it all hasn't come to an end? What if, after it's all over, there will be never-ending darkness and quiet, but I will still want to eat and stretch my back? What is the essential difference between being and nothingness? Is it simply the fact of my being able to ask that question? *Cogito, ergo.* . . .

S. Cat lifts his head. The box is still sealed, but he can feel a change in the air. It feels like the moment just before a thunderstorm when every creature pauses to listen to electricity building in the atmosphere. All of his being is focused, as if his life has had a single purpose that will culminate in this one instant. Then, something strange and special happens. S. Cat can see into the future. Not very far—maybe a second or less—and he can see himself following two paths. One is bright and verdant and as familiar as a memory. The other is dark. Silent. Revealing nothing. He is two cats now, his consciousness flickering. There is a flash of light. It could be the lid of the box being opened. It could be the radioactive nucleus decaying, chucking a newborn photon into the toxic vial. In that strange fleeting instant what comes to his mind is the caption of the Paul Gauguin painting, restated in the first-person: *Where do I come from? What am I? Where am I going?*

HOW TO ASSEMBLE AN ATOMIC BOMB

Your best and wisest refuge from all troubles
is in your science.

—Ada Lovelace

WAS RAISED IN THE SUBURBS TWO DECADES AFTER THE END OF WORLD WAR II, IN A JEWISH HOME PAINTED BROWN FOR SURVIVOR'S GUILT. It was a home where joy cowered in the shadows like a troubled child whom we loved but could not tolerate. My parents always seemed to be atoning for something—a dessert consumed, a moment lost to idleness, a dollar spent frivolously. In my household, every day was Yom Kippur.

It was the late 1960s and the Cold War was still too warm for comfort. My town conducted tests of public safety sirens at noon every Thursday, when huge speakers mounted on utility poles at parks and schools would emit a series of adenoidal whines. To me, they were simply an annoying curiosity, a relic from an era occasionally portrayed on television. But to my parents and grandparents, who had left siblings behind in Poland, Lithuania, Ukraine, Hungary, or anywhere the great swath of murder cast its shadow, the sound turned their stomachs to water. During this exercise, my classmates and I were led single file to the elementary school basement in which we would, I now presume, wait out the nuclear winter.

As an eight-year-old boy growing up in that environment, I had a smorgasbord of neuroses to choose from: that I might be pruned by anti-Semitism like other branches of my family tree, or drafted into the army and sent to Vietnam, or, if I managed to survive all of that, that nuclear missiles might rain from the sky with precisely twenty-two minutes' warning. The litany of evils perpetrated in the war was proof enough that God had walked away from his desk while The Bomb stepped in to assume His authority.

At the same time, just as The Bomb was a signal that our lives could be unfairly attenuated, my family watched the Space Race with a feeling of optimism, following the *Apollo* launches with breathless excitement. We took sugar cubes infused with polio vaccine. We brought lighter, more compact tools into our homes and watched in amazement as vacuum tubes gave way to microchips and diaphanous liquid crystal. I chose high-tech heroes to protect me from the things I feared. Astro Boy, the robot from space who had jets for feet and lasers in his fingers, could fly from crisis to crisis to save young people from monsters and evildoers. Speed Racer, in his powerful Mach V, who turned petrochemical energy into high-velocity action only an eight-year-old could love. The escape of television brought solace while I grew into an adult, and it gave me hope that someday I could take my place behind a desk, holding paper and chalk and tools of craftsmanship and art, and banish thoughts of perishing in a squalid oubliette.

The drama of my forebears and the threat of The Bomb made it impossible to imagine having an ordinary life. Even the simple hope of having children was influenced by the context of my youth. I could not simply be a dad who had kids: I had an obligation to bring better people into the world and give them an opportunity to improve it.

After a year of failing to get Ruby pregnant, we had to accept that I was less virile and she less fecund than either of us had hoped. Ruby, after all, with her generous, curvy body, was built for baby-making. She was a fifth child with fourteen cousins, who had hit puberty at eleven and thereafter lit the candle of every male within a mile, who dreamed of raising an enormous family of her own. She never suspected, at thirty-three, that she would be last in line to have kids. So, the onus fell on me, the second boy in a family of bright but sexually weak men, to determine whether I was, in fact, producing the necessary ingredients to make my wife pregnant.

As children of the atomic age, we learned to heal disillusionment by turning to science. If we had been born in any other age, Ruby and I would have taken our fertility problems as a personal affront, thinking perhaps that

God had overlooked us, that Ruby had been born to some innate state of sin. We may have dined regularly on stimulating foods: oysters, shark fin, the balls of a bull, or the penis of a goat. It is hard to imagine that any enlightened person at any time in history could take these remedies seriously. It is more likely that people turned to them as a last resort, after they noticed that they had been forgotten by the saints and angels.

In the Age of Information, we would give our bodies to science, let medical professionals treat our bodies like machines, turn the tables on mysticism and myth. Instead of prayer and *gourmandise*, we prepared to give under to technology. We would lie beneath bright lights and allow ourselves to be probed by metallic instruments. I would hand over samples of my most private juices while Ruby opened her legs for a speculum and catheter. We would accept these insults with grace, welcoming them without objection. If we were to let science come through the door, we would have to chuck our taboos out the window.

At the clinic, a lab-coated technician behind the desk was tired and bored. She took my name and address, insurance card number, telephone number, blood type, and age. I saw no signs of squeamishness or judgment in her eyes. She may have been in charge of collecting semen, but she was as bland as a bureaucrat. She shoved a white paper bag across the counter and mumbled that the official collection room was busy. I could wait, or I could do my business in the supply closet. She left it up to me. I had no desire to sit in a waiting room, avoiding eye contact with people who knew exactly what I was waiting for. So, I took the specimen kit into the closet and pushed the door closed behind me.

The paper bag contained a sterile specimen cup wrapped in plastic, an alcohol swab, and a small sheet of paper printed with instructions:

1. Clean head of penis with alcohol swab and wait until completely dry.
2. Use the cup to collect the specimen.
3. Cover the cup and write your name and the date and time on the label affixed to the cup.
4. Bring the cup back to the lab technician.

One wall of the room was taken up with shelving. Stationery. Boxes of sterile latex gloves. A large photocopier was wedged along the back wall, facing the door. The irony of producing a semen sample in a copy room was not lost on me. I wondered, had my tacit acceptance of using biotechnology to conceive a child brought me a step closer to the antiseptic future of *Brave New World*? If my child can be conceived in a Petri dish, will my grandchildren gestate in a mason jar and enter the world fully formed without having passed through a human birth canal? If my pursuit of becoming a parent requires a more intimate relationship with laboratory equipment than with my own wife's body, will I (and my children) lose something essential about being human?

I got to work, leaning against the photocopier, praying not to be interrupted by someone feeling a sudden need for paper clips. With a shallow hiccup, the job was done. I put the cover on the cup and the cup in the bag and walked out of the closet with as much insouciance as I could manage.

I could have given any of my other personal fluids—urine, spit, snot, blood. I could have taken a local anesthetic to donate spinal fluid or marrow. I could have cried my eyes out and let the tears collect in a test tube. Why did giving this specimen make me feel so dirty? Surely there is nothing inherently shameful about a tiny gob of spunk in a cup. My embarrassment came from its evocation of awkward adolescence, the conversion of ejaculation from transcendent climax to process of elimination, the separation of the church of medicine from the state of pleasure.

A week later, the results came back in a standard anonymous business envelope. A daunting collection of numbers and acronyms arranged in tabular format accompanied by the doctor's analysis. As it turned out, there were very few actual sperm in my semen, and the small population they found were swimming well under the speed limit. Given this state of affairs, the note read, it was unlikely that I could make anyone pregnant—not a younger woman, not a Greek fertility goddess, not a reckless nymphomaniac (were they reading my mind?) and certainly not my thirty-three-year-old wife. But there was still hope. There are ways to raise the sperm count and tip the chances of knocking someone up by ordinary means, without resorting to assisted reproductive technology. It suggested I follow some simple guidelines for six weeks and then repeat the test.

There they were again, more officious instructions printed on a simple white sheet:

> consider boxers instead of briefs; avoid hot baths; avoid alcohol, caffeine, and recreational drug use; avoid biking, horseback riding, and skiing. Consider taking 80mg zinc oxide and 1000mg vitamin C once a day.

This was a set of guidelines so unscientific they could have come from the arcane mysticism of Middle Earth. Hundreds of people with finely educated minds have worked on the problem of infertility for centuries. Thousands of lab rats have given their lives for reproductive research. Biotechnology companies have crafted delicate tools to perform arthroscopic procedures, experimented with pharmacological formulations, conducted mass studies and published their results in the most respected scientific journals, and this is what they came up with: change my underwear and eat an orange.

What biology needs is a revolution similar to the discovery of the quantum. That revolution led to a wholesale upheaval of the way science was practiced. It called for a rewriting of physical laws, an adjustment of the worldviews held by entire cultures, not just by a few scientists. Quantum physics readjusted our definition of matter and space, and led to a reevaluation of astronomy and cosmology, and an entirely new creation story.

Perhaps the discovery of DNA provides a similar tipping point in biology. The Human Genome Project (the HGP) discovered the canonical ordering of three billion base pairs in the human genome, and the bulk of the work of mapping those sequences to actual functions in the body remains unfinished. In a sense, the HGP came at a perfect time. It is the biology project for the information age, being all about decryption and decoding and impossible to accomplish without computers with vast amounts of storage and organizational capacity. The end result is a better understanding of rules—not chemistry or physics, but the pure information—that molecules use to organize themselves into living organisms.

If any epiphanies came of the HGP they have been ontological. We learned that our bodies are built from basic materials, that every living thing is composed of the same list of ingredients combined using very slightly different recipes. The instructions for building a human being differ in only minor ways from the ones for building a gorilla or a mouse or a kangaroo. They are as similar as a Bundt cake and a Christmas cookie. Moreover, the number of genes that separate one human being from another are fewer than a handful, regardless of one's race or personal history. In terms of the human genotype, we are more or less all alike. In addition to the purely medical benefits of decoding the genome, the philosophically significant outcome of the HGP might be that, on the whole, empathy increases.

Decoding and reprogramming genes lets us look at bodies with the same objectivity as we examine other machines. They can be manipulated, controlled, perhaps even created, by purely mechanical means. Since our definition of God is that which holds the tools to create, sustain, and restore life, we become like gods when we perform those holy acts. When we relinquish control of our bodies to man-made tools and procedures, we turn the machines themselves into deities.

This, alas, is what we allowed to happen with The Bomb.

I grew up with the man-as-machine theme on Saturday mornings, in my pajamas watching cartoons. Charming *Looney Tunes* characters could be squashed by an anvil, blown to bits by TNT, or spattered with lead from a blunderbuss, to emerge dazed but never completely destroyed. Their bodies were as durable as steel. In *Hypo-Chondri-Cat*, a Chuck Jones cartoon from 1950, two mischievous mice practice their own zany form of medicine on the poor cat named Claude, first with a timber saw, then with kitchen implements—an eggbeater, a chef's knife. Claude emerges unharmed, on the whole. Having been bested by a pair of mice, his ego was more bruised than his body. In the 1950s and 1960s, we had gotten past any sense of alienation and had become fascinated with, even inspired by, the possibilities that man-as-machine offers. These ideas persist in the popularity of fictions such as *Neuromancer* and *The Matrix*. At my own alma mater, the MIT Media Laboratory, geeks in the "Wearables" and "Biomechatronics" departments voluntarily wire their bodies to computers in search of a perfect union.

The man-god-machine theme predates transistors and Saturday morning cartoons by a long shot. The story of Icarus and Daedalus is a man-god-machine myth that ends in tragedy. Mary Shelley wrote the novel *Frankenstein* at the height of the Industrial Revolution, at a time when there was a great interest in alchemy, the search for a "life force," and a belief that one could create life by esoteric means not requiring a biological reproductive system. The 1931 film with Boris Karloff as the creature is embedded in our cultural ethos. The scenes in which The Doctor (John Clive) works at creating life using industrial-age instruments and galvanic forces have become the images of reference for mad scientists who abuse technology for questionable purposes. And where Frankenstein's monster was the product of man-as-god, Charlie Chaplin captured the poignancy of man's fate at the hands of the machine-as-god in *Modern Times*, his 1938 Marxist allegory. In the most enduring scenes, he gets caught up in the gears of the Big Machine, which bear a close resemblance to the gears of his own film camera; gets stuck repeating a bolt-tightening motion from overwork on the assembly line; and is secured into a feeding machine, a device that pushes food into his mouth to provide him with the fuel he needs to keep working.

Where religion teaches us that the body is a vessel for a soul, science banishes the soul to the realm of fantasy, explaining it away as a hallucination brought on by the elusive twitching of the central nervous system. The proposition that the body is a machine is so firmly entrenched in the modern worldview that it seems incontrovertible. What else could it be, we ask with sardonic arrogance. Just look at the evidence. But the so-called evidence is relatively new. From Aristotle onward, people tended to see the body as a manifestation of an intangible animus, the organs being interesting but on the whole inconsequential portions of meat, at best the loci of autonomous spiritual qualities like emotion and love. The soul-body and mind-body problems are two ways of addressing the same reductionist question. Are we spirits or machines, sacred or profane, or some irreconcilable combination of the two? We wake up every morning with our dreams fresh in our minds, naked and quivering with their echoes, yet we also accept the philosophy that we can say nothing more about consciousness or spiritual experience than can be traced to an event in our bodies. There is no satisfying answer to this dilemma. If we propose that our thoughts and emotions are illusory artifacts of bioelectrical impulses, we have abnegated the essential motivating quality of life.

Ruby's round of humiliation was scheduled a week after mine, in the form of a hysterosalpingogram, a procedure for looking inside her fallopian tubes to see if there were any blockages. There's no telling what could have gotten in there to gum things up. The procedure was intended to dislodge whatever lint or dust bunnies or bits of dinner leftovers were in the way, thereby avoiding the possibility of a painful and potentially fatal ectopic pregnancy.

I stood in an air-conditioned control booth looking through a plate glass window at Ruby, who was prone on an operating table in the basement of the clinic. The booth was hushed and as inviting as the deck of the starship *Enterprise*, subtly lit by the blue glow of instrumentation. I was joined in the booth by the radiologist, a man with a Band-Aid on his chin and a burn on the back of his hand, neither of which inspired in me much confidence of his ability to control his tools. He spoke to the nurses through a microphone, and they doted on Ruby on the other side of the glass. Their voices came back through a set of stereo speakers.

Ruby, draped in hospital blues, was making her usual jokes. "After this, I think I'll have the facial," she said.

The nurses cracked up. "She's a quick one," they agreed.

I could sense they were relieved to have a patient with a sense of humor. Most patients become anxious, and their stress comes out as crabbiness or a string of irrelevant questions, or, mostly, just silence. It is a natural reaction to lying naked under spotlights, in a dark room in the bowels of a hospital, surrounded by masked faces, gloved hands manipulating your body. The experience is too similar to the first and last moments of life. What the nurses did not know is that Ruby responds to intimidating situations by keeping her mind engaged, and by making a connection with the other people in the room. She is only comfortable once she has incapacitated someone with laughter.

Ruby received a syringe of Iodine 131, a radioactive dye that has a sixty-day half-life. The point of the procedure was to activate the dye to make her fallopian tubes glow like the fluorescent sign outside a diner. If there were any blockages in the shadows, the keen eye of the doctor's ray machine would surely find them. The neutrons from the iodine knocked into the atoms that made up her uterine wall, the fallopian channel, and her ovaries, and they responded by winking out a photon or two. Was there any danger in bombarding Ruby's eggs with neutrons before they were fertilized? Would the subatomic vibrations reconfigure their DNA to instruct our child's body to grow a tail or extra fingers, or turn my progeny into a family of free radicals? With poetic irony, the principles that gave us The Bomb would help Ruby to conceive.

I could see Ruby's insides on a television screen mounted into the wall. The main characters of this particular cartoon were two cloudy dandelion heads poking out of a mushroom. There was no sound, and nobody was getting smooshed with an anvil. I was tempted to change the channel, but the radiologist had returned to the operating chamber and was holding the remote. He made a few small adjustments and then told the nurses to skedaddle. They exited the room through a leaden door, leaving Ruby alone in the chamber.

"Hold your breath," he told Ruby through the microphone.

The doctor's paw pressed the big red button on the control panel. The lights dimmed; the room shuddered. A blast of steam engulfed the gurney. Snakes of electricity leaped from the bald heads of Van de Graaff generators. The nurses descended on Ruby with a whisk, a Kitchen-Aid, a pool cue, then an earnest Basset Hound came lumbering through the door bearing a cask of whiskey to revive her.

"Hold your breath," he whispered through the microphone.

The doctor's burned hand pressed the big red button on the control panel. Ruby sat bolt upright and waved her arms about, screaming. "Astro Boy, save me! Oh, save me, Astro Boy!" The television flickered, and my robot hero appeared, earnest and strong. He flew out of the screen, lasers blazing.

The doctor's finger pressed a big red button on the

control panel. Ruby held her breath. There was a brief and quiet hum as the X-ray machine took a snapshot of her sloshy insides. Then it was over. The doctor spoke through the microphone again, telling Ruby to relax, and the nurses moved in with swift confidence to clean her up.

The results of our tests were undeniable. Ruby had no discernible flaws. Her eggs were still fresh. We were the perfect candidates for in-vitro fertilization, but we would be compelled to grasp the hand of technology, even as it threatened us with its other fist. The Bomb came in an unexpected form. It rained chaos, tearing Ruby and me apart particle by particle, scattering the shards to all directions, forcing us to run for cover. We saw a path and we took to it swiftly, knowing we had found an uncertain way to escape annihilation. If there was a technological solution to our existential problem, we would take it. We had no choice.

The drills and the fearmongering and the war talk established that the moments of my life were precious and numbered. I had grown up convinced that I would not live long enough to know children and grandchildren, that I would bear witness to humanity's last few hours. I was not aware of it then, but only the birth of my child would reestablish my faith in the future.

. . . what I'd like to know is what moves inside us and where does it go, no, I'm not talking about worms, microbes, bacteria, those living creatures that inhabit us, I'm referring to something else, to something that moves and perhaps moves us at the same time, just as constellation, galaxy, solar system, sun, earth, sea . . . move and move us with them, what is the name, finally, of the thing that moves all the rest, from one end of the chain to the other, or perhaps there is no chain and the universe is a ring, at once so thin that apparently only we and what is inside us fit into it and so thick that it can accommodate the maximum dimension of the universe, which is the ring itself, what is the name of what follows after us. The nonvisible begins with man, came the surprising answer. . . .

—Jose Saramago, *The Stone Raft*

GOD, IN THE FORM OF A YOUNG CHINESE MAN WEARING HOSPITAL BLUES AND A BEATIFIC SMILE, SAT BEHIND A DESK SCATTERED WITH SCIENTIFIC RESEARCH PAPERS. The walls of his office glowed from the Sun, which he had arranged in a convenient location outside his window. The light reflected off diplomas from the most prestigious North American medical schools and societies. He had seen it all before —a desperate couple of a certain age who had tried to conceive in the original way, only to learn that their bodies were lacking the divine spark. We were here to express our hunger for a little taste of immortality as manifested in a child of our loins. God listened to our plaint with paternal compassion.

"You have made love in the manner I have told you?" he asked.

Yes, we replied.

"Have you lain with each other on the prescribed days, and in the humblest of positions?"

Yes.

"Have you eaten only of the nutritious foods I have listed for you? And clothed yourselves in a manner that is loose-fitting and inviting to child?"

That part was easy. We had become vegetarians to cleanse our bodies, and I had switched to boxers the previous summer because they kept my gonads cooler. Ruby had admitted her coffee dependency and had been on the wagon for six weeks. We had made an unwitting transformation from brooding carnivores comfortable in tight, black jeans and smoke-filled cafés to baggy-waisted hypochondriacs with an unnatural fear of exposure to toxins, depressants, preservatives, or stress. Our reading habits had changed, too. Our night tables, once piled high with the likes of Henry Miller,

Lawrence Durrell, Marguerite Duras, seemed to have taken on a singular purpose. My café-culture self would be appalled at the titles: *Eggs and Seeds—the Infertility Diet; The Empty Womb; Overcoming the Anguish of Infertility; Sixty Days to Total Wellness.*

We may not have had the wherewithal to carry off a miracle ourselves, but our deity and his clinic prescribed a special mix of pharmaceuticals that would help us to conjure one. Ruby and I had taken our fair share of drugs in our teens and twenties. Ruby was familiar with the potency of LSD and psilocybin, had visited other universes where those chemicals take you. With ecstasy, I was able to levitate, glide along the streets in a parallel dimension of concentrated bonhomie. Neither of us was prepared for the effects of fertility potions. Human follicle-stimulating hormones are not heroin or absinthe. They will not relax her, intrigue her, or prepare her body to win the Tour de France. They will produce headaches, nausea, bloating and cramps, weepiness, volatility, and spite. Ruby's ovaries will grow to the size of tangerines, each one stocked with more eggs than a New York diner.

To make this all work, her internal temperature must be neither too high nor too low, the eggs must be ripened just so, and a single sperm, the Chosen One, must be in just the right place in the fallopian tube at just the right time during her cycle. One perfect sperm, not too stupid to swim in the right direction, determined to keep swimming even when there is no end in sight, must persevere and find the egg without benefit of a map or GPS or even a sweet voice calling it homeward. Once all of these things have happened, only then can the precarious process of conception begin.

In Cambridge, Massachusetts, a team of cosmologists ponder the uncanny balance among the forces that govern the behavior of atomic nuclei and stars. Some forces cause objects in the universe to drift apart, while others hold matter together. They are so finely balanced that, had any of them been off by even one in ten-million, life could not have come about. Their observations imply that everything that happens, absolutely everywhere, is part of a vast chain reaction that was set in motion fourteen billion years ago, mitigated by natural constraints, that must play out in a specific order so that we can exist to ponder it. Consider the birth and death of stars, the rise and fall of civilizations, the accidental drip on the edge of a wine bottle as it is poured. I will not claim that anything we observe is preordained, but it is tempting to imagine every event being a necessary antecedent of another. There are many paths forward, but only one way back.

Life can only exist on planets not too near, not too far from stars. Stars can only hold planets in their orbit because of the strength of gravity. Gravity behaves the way it does because—well, because it does, and we hope it always will. It may seem like a shallow tautology to claim that the only universe we can observe is one that sustains life, but this statement, called the anthropic principle, has been discussed in a serious way by a handful of philosophers and scientists. Some say if the universe had been any different, life could not have developed, and we would not be here to observe it. Turning this proposition on its head, one could logically propose that no universe can exist without life arising in it. This is a bit stronger than the first claim because it says life is a necessary post-condition to any universe similar to our own. That is, the appearance of life is as fundamental a law as gravity or electromagnetism.

So, it would seem the odds were stacked in our favor when it came to having a child. The universe was designed to support life. Perhaps the new life we yearned for just needed a metaphysical nudge. We tried meditation, acupuncture, positive thinking. Nothing worked. Pep talks, group therapy, tantric sex, chi-gong, Tony Robbins tapes, EST, Scientology. Still nothing. I woke myself up at two a.m., and then again at four, to change an imaginary diaper on an imaginary infant. Still no luck. In the seventeenth century, philosopher Bishop George Berkeley proposed that the world only exists as an artifact of our own perceptions. If we change what we perceive, we change reality. This idea might be effective on your own body if you are an athlete or a cancer survivor. Not so much when you're trying to create a new life. It was disheartening to run up against the limits of philosophy.

God said, "You have been diligent and careful, and it is obvious to me that you are deserving. This child you seek will not come easily. Your hopes will be raised and then dashed, and you will feel like giving up. But try to remain positive. Your attitude can have an effect on the outcome. We are going to try a round of in-vitro fertilization. I'd say your chances are good."

Then He said something that chilled me to the bone, for it cast doubt on his omnipotence.

He said, "I'll do my best, of course. But there are no guarantees."

The King of Kings asked Ruby to leave the room, so He could consult with me in private. When we were alone, He commanded me to rise before Him and pull my trousers to my knees. I was but a sheep, and He was my master.

"I'm going to check you for a varicocele—a narrowing of the blood vessels in the testes, which can lower the sperm count. It's quite common and easily repaired if you have it."

Now the Hand of God was on my balls, feeling among the folds like an inventor checking the tightness of a concealed nut. His eyes were pointed heavenward, His fingers asserting just the right amount of pressure to reassure me that this was all benediction and no grope. My heart quickened. I held my breath. Hardly was His hand upon me when He stepped back and indicated that I should cover my shame with my Gap Authentic Skinnys. He opened the door to His sanctum and beckoned

Ruby to return.

"Well, your husband does not have a varicocele, which means you are both good candidates for treatment. You will begin next week. I will put together a dossier and tell my staff. You will receive excellent care. They're really angels. You may not see me again for a while. But please call if you have questions."

The audience was over.

The religious among us believe with all their hearts that God is an active participant in the world. They feel His presence as real as the warmth of sunshine on a spring day, as reliable as the pull of gravity. But what if they are wrong? He might have set the universe in motion and then taken the nearest exit. He could have assembled the physical laws, created the space-time fabric, ignited the Big Bang, then absented Himself, so He could go start trouble elsewhere. Such a God would be omnipotent but not omniscient. He would have created the principles through which the universe operates, but have no foreknowledge of the consequences. Such a God may not be present today, but His genius could still be observed. The conduct of science is our attempt at appreciating His creation. Through careful, diligent effort, we creep from revelation to tiny revelation, inching along an endless path of truth. And a truly beautiful aspect of this pursuit is that every answer raises more questions.

Our day at the clinic filled Ruby and me with optimism. We stayed awake until past midnight surfing the web for articles about fertility treatments, marveling at the odd language of the acolytes—unfamiliar words and unpronounceable acronyms. Intrauterine Insemination. Intracytoplasmic Sperm Injection. Gamete Intrafallopian Transfer. When we finally went to bed, we lay on our backs, Ruby's head on my arm, staring up into the dark. As we talked about families and babies, I imagined infants in the darkness, floating just out of arm's reach above me. If I reached out far enough, I could feel their tiny bellies graze my fingertips, maybe even grasp a chubby thigh and pull it down to lie next to me, warm and squirming against my skin.

The darkness became sleep and sleep became morning and light filtered through the leaves outside our window, painting dappled rosettes on Ruby's face. Her eyes were shut, and her lips curled into a gentle smile that, for the first time in months, looked like the natural relaxed state to which they would return when she exerted no effort. I had only seen her like this when she was dreaming of food—something simple like breakfast cereal or chicken schnitzel—but this morning her first words were, "Good morning, Papa." When Ruby is certain of something, even a thing that has not happened yet, she is often right. So, on that morning in the kitchen, still in our pajamas, drinking chai, I afforded myself the luxury of *The New York Times* crossword while she meandered around the web.

I lifted my eyes for a moment to notice how Ruby's spoon was balanced on the lip of her plate so that it seemed to hover over the table. She had left it there without thinking, and I was about to remark on it when she said, "Hey, look at this article."

She read aloud,

> Artificial sperm have been used to create living animals for the first time, in an experiment that promises to pave the way for a new era of fertility treatment. Seven mouse pups, six of which survived to adulthood, were born in a laboratory in Germany after scientists fertilized eggs with sperm that had been grown from embryonic stem cells. The births provide the strongest evidence yet that it will eventually be possible to use ES cells to treat infertile men who make no sperm of their own.[1]

---

[1] *London Times*, July 10, 2006

It was not the fact that stem cells were used that I found chilling, nor the fact that the pups survived to birth, but the possibility that human evolution as we knew it may be over. These poor, little, blind mouse pups, soft and wriggling in the wood chips at the bottom of their mother's cage, are the end of a genetic line. For, once it is possible to construct sperm and egg from stem cells, sex is no longer necessary. With its obsolescence, natural selection will go the way of the dinosaurs. One day we will reproduce ourselves eugenically in Petri dishes—not because it is more convenient or fun or morally better, but because, as natural fertility decreases and technology pampers our human passion for perfection and control, we will lose our desire to leave reproduction in the untrustworthy hands of nature. One day long in the future we will look back at our mushy, sex-crazed past, and we will marvel at how far we have come without lamenting the chaos and uncertainty we have lost.

Embryonic stem cells are part of the blastocyst, the earliest stages of a creature before it looks like the person or mouse or bird or Komodo dragon it will eventually become. Somehow, the blastocyst grows into a fetus with a head, a tail, cute little fingers or talons, bones, eyes and brains, and a remarkable collection of organs. All embryonic cells might look similar, but later in development, they specialize. All neurons and red blood cells and skin, all flesh and lips and hair, are the progeny of the few cells that were present at the beginning. The trick in the mouse experiment was to coax the early cells to develop into sperm instead of, say, eyeballs, by doping them with the right kinds of enzymes and proteins.

It would appear that stem cells are the most perfect life form we have yet discovered. More adaptable than a roach. More fecund than a bacterium. More mysterious and influential than the head of the Federal Reserve. An embryonic stem cell's penchant for transmutation recalls the far-fetched Silly Putty shapeshifters of science fiction. But also, in their role as universal seed, they strengthen the argument that life developed on Earth during its searing inhospitable infancy. To top it off, these truly wonderful cells now originate in Ruby's ovaries. Her body can produce stem cells with the simple addition of some chromosomal material. It doesn't even have to come from me. We could, theoretically, and if it were legal, snip a little DNA from almost anyone's skin or hair, subject it to extraction and purification, then inject it carefully inside the cytoplasm of one of her eggs. A few days later, we could harvest the blastocyst to create almost any kind of living tissue.

Ruby wondered aloud, what is the point in undergoing a desperate procedure like IVF if, in a few years, we will be able to order a baby by mail? We could send in a couple of DNA samples. They would take an artificial egg from a carton, then squirt your genes and mine into the center, and plant it in a mechanical uterus. With a little luck and a prayer (genuflect and gestate), it would grow into a healthy fetus. When it was big enough, the fetus could graduate to a liquid incubator—I'm imagining a sort of fish tank filled with a concoction of artificial amniotic fluid and maybe a few toys to keep the kid happy. Maybe they could pipe in Mozart, project some flashcards into it for a head start on reading. A couple of months later, we'd come in and pay with a debit card. That's it. No morning sickness, no cramping, no bloating, no waddling, sore feet, head rushes, cravings, pain, blood, or screaming. Just, hello, I ordered a baby to take out. I mean, why not wait for that?

Because, my dear, before you go all Aldous Huxley on me, I will remind you that the technology is not mature. Perhaps in fifty years, such a scenario will be possible. But by then, despite our daily consumption of omega-threes and diligent application of moisturizing unguents, we will be too old to raise the poor kid. But the day is coming, and if we have a child now and raise him right, we will one day have the delightful privilege of designing a few grandchildren.

Our human form is a snapshot of a long process that started over six-hundred-million years ago when the first organic chemicals met in the Precambrian goo. We ask how we came to be so perfect, so much like ourselves. But the answer is that we are the only way we can be, and no other way. The biological anthropic principle is the same as the cosmological one. We are only intelligent enough to ask how we came to exist because early cell biology and genetics followed a certain path. If early conditions had been any different, we might still be living in the ocean.

The manner in which the physical forces hold matter together while keeping suns and planets apart is among the most intractable mysteries in cosmology. It would appear that everything has to be exactly as it is, or it cannot exist at all. While the nature of the physical forces, so finely tuned, gives us clues as to where the universe may have come from and where it is going, here we are snug in our little corner where life is not only likely, but unavoidable. We perceive the universe as it is because we are part of it. Every perception, every moment of living is a note in a private symphony that, with its clanging and clamoring, its joyous harmonies and plangent noise, creates an illusion of a world outside of ourselves. When in the course of our blind meanderings we happen to touch another person and share a phrase or two, our internal worlds are augmented by a glimpse into an entirely different cosmos. So, when a child is born, it's not simply that we have created the universe anew: every newborn child is a universe unto himself.

> *O, wonder! How many goodly creatures are there here! How beauteous mankind is! O, brave new world That has such people in't!*

ENTANGLEMENT

But what if they were told that the body of the deity is not composed of indivisible particles? I mean to say that it is not composed of substances resembling those that . . . He creates, but is one continuous body not admitting division except in fantasy. For you imagine in a similar way that the body of heaven admits of being divided and split up, whereas the philosopher maintains that this possibility of division is only due to the action of imagination. . . .

—Maimonides, *The Guide of the Perplexed*

THERE WAS A CLOCK IN THE ROOM. It hung on the wall across from Ruby's hospital bed, about two-thirds of the way up to the ceiling. Through a window, I could see the river and the tangle of roads that hugged its edge and crossed its bridges. It was early spring, and the trees were still mostly bald, though a few tender chartreuse buds could be seen poking out of a branch here and there. Later in the season, it would have been harder to see the river and the roads. A mature canopy would have made the room more intimate. With the leaves gone, daylight marched into the room with promise. It was the clock on the wall across from the bed that held my attention. An industrial clock, about ten inches in diameter with a white background and numbers printed in black around its circumference. The minute and second hands were long and elegant as a piano player's fingers, the hour hand stubby and lazy. This clock reminded me of the ones in my elementary school classrooms, the ones I watched with growing impatience until classes ended at a clumsy ten-minutes-till or twenty-five-minutes past. Those clocks were interconnected by a mysterious electromechanical force that allowed them to be synchronized from a command post next to the principal's office. I would be watching the sweep hand tick away the seconds, enjoying the way it sprung like a cat from one tick to the next, quivering for just a tiny moment while it counted one one-thousand, ready for its next second's leap. Then, without any warning, the minute hand would begin to swing wildly around. The hour hand would follow, brushing away the hours as fast as my pulse. School's out. Dinner time. Homework. Bedtime. Night. Bus arrives. Math. English. Lunch. Finally, the clock would stop its crazy ride, and the hands would freeze just a few minutes before or after their origin. The second hand would begin its ticking again like nothing had happened. I half expected the clock across from Ruby's hospital bed to do the same thing. But after a few hours of spying on it, I realized it didn't matter. Time is a fickle, inconsistent measure of the events in our lives, and we don't need a clock to prove that.

We had arrived at eight-thirty in the evening. Two hours thirty-five minutes earlier, we had been seated at our favorite diner. Ruby was uncomfortable on the banquette, mad at her pregnant belly for the way it got between her and a plate of corned-beef hash. We chewed without saying much. Our minds were preoccupied with the arrangements we were making for when the baby came. My parents had given us an old-fashioned perambulator with white wheels and a retractable hood, as opulent and comfortable as the carriage that brought Princess Diana to Westminster Abbey on her wedding day. It was spring, and we were looking forward to strolling the baby along the leafy streets of West Cambridge, our pride and delight exceeding our exhaustion.

Ruby looked down at her lap with alarm and said, "I think I spilled my soup." I pulled a wad of napkins from the dispenser on the table and handed them across to her before we both realized her mistake. We hadn't ordered soup. Her water had broken. Ruby looked up at me and laughed an elated, nervous "Hah!" I helped her out of the banquette and walked her toward the exit. As we paid the check, Ruby couldn't resist one more quip. She asked the person operating the cash register, "Do you deliver?"

We returned home to collect her things, feed the cat, make the house tidy for our return. We pulled Ruby's overnight bag out of the closet, where we had stashed it three weeks earlier. She took my hand.

"When we come back, we will be a family," she said.

We knew how to be two together. I wondered what it would be like to be three. Even now, with Ruby's belly as large as it ever would be, with her skirt in the laundry basket stained with amniotic fluid, I still did not believe that I was going to be a parent, and that a large part of our life was now over. I was afraid that we would become one of those messy, preoccupied couples, a pair of bores who talk of nothing but baby gear and sleep deprivation, or that my relationship with my wife and child might not survive because I would be unfit as a father. A part of me believed that Ruby would have been better off without me, should have taken her cue from the black widow spider by getting rid of me as soon as she got pregnant. In a panic it occurred to me that I had reached a stupendous level of arrogance by assuming I had the capacity to care for a human being no larger than a *pain Poilâne*. I needed confidence, support, proof that I would not be an utter fuck-up as a dad. But of course, proof never comes when you need it most. Images of our early relationship flashed through my mind. Our years in the Paris apartment. A train trip to Italy. Dinner parties. Long, quiet nights lying on that sofa, our legs entwined, reading our books. As I stood in the doorway, I tried to send a message back to our earlier selves. Enjoy it, I told myself. It will not last.

Ruby squeezed my hand. "It's a new chapter," she said.

We closed the door and drove to the hospital.

Quantum entanglement is a phenomenon in which two or more subatomic particles appear to act as a single system. The condition of one particle in an entangled pair allows us to infer the condition of the other. Two photons, Alpha and Beta, traveling away from each other, appear to be in cahoots, always maintaining equal and opposite momentum. The particles appear to behave in harmony with each other, regardless of the distance between them.

We become entangled in our relationships with our lovers, our siblings, our children. We seem to be entangled when a sense of urgency or dread comes over us, and we pick up the phone to call a dear friend, and the first words out of her mouth are, "Oh! I was just about to call you, or send you an email—such-and-such terrible thing has happened to me." Twins appear to be entangled when, in Baltimore and Seattle, they propose to their fiancées on the same day. These occurrences are mere coincidence, kismet, freak accidents. We laugh them off in the same manner as we dismiss ESP or communication with space aliens because our culture of science requires a phenomenon to be repeatable before it can be accepted as fact. Human entanglement is not verifiable, but it does repeat.

The clock on the wall read nine-twenty. Outside, the traffic had slowed to a halt. The river was adorned with a necklace of lights, red on one side, white on the other. It had become harder to see past my own reflection in the window, so I closed the venetian blinds with a clack. Ruby, doped on a sedative called Nubain, muttered, "Don't wake the baby." The baby was, indeed, asleep, curled up warm and safe inside her uterus, not ready to budge. Ruby's body was sending encouraging waves outward and downward with brief contractions every three or four minutes. These tender hugs were nothing compared to the Big Squeeze that was to come.

Ruby and I have been playing make-believe with this child since he was conceived, though secretly I imagined a teenager in there, complete with skateboard and phone. Ruby chortled every time he shifted positions. We gloated over ghostly ultrasounds of him curled up like a shrimp, sucking his thumb. We fed Ruby healthy, nutritious foods, and she eschewed coffee and alcohol without complaint. I read to him at night, my head on Ruby's belly, lowering my voice to a paternal register, hoping to plant the suggestion that I was a comforting presence, and not the weak, incompetent father I was sure I would become. Like religious zealots, we focused a large portion of emotional energy on something we had never seen, a person who did not exist except in faith. When he changed positions after Ruby ate an Indian meal, we said he didn't like cumin. When he slept as we watched the movie *Amadeus*, we said he loved classical music. When it was three days after his due date and Ruby still had not become adequately effaced, we said for certain he was going to have a quiet disposition and love his mother.

When do Baby and Ruby stop being one person and become two? When the umbilical cord is cut? When he pops out of her vagina like a watermelon seed pressed between wet fingers? Or much, much earlier, as a fetus, a zygote, a few-celled oocyte? This question is at the center of a heated moral debate, but the question itself is flawed. Mother and child are entangled from the moment the woman realizes she is pregnant, and they remain so forever.

The Nubain drip sang sweet lullabies to Ruby's insides, making her drowsy. There was not much in this room except the clock, the bed, a small linen closet for swaddling blankets, and a stainless-steel sink with those duck-paddle faucet handles one operates with the back of a hand. On the wall opposite the bed was a tiny antiseptic toilet, and in the corner near the headboard, a vinyl-covered easy chair. I sat in the chair, tilting my head back to stare at the ceiling. The room was dark, and Ruby was snoring. I counted seventy-five identical dark spots on each of the four ceiling tiles directly above my head, then began to drift into my own version of a narcotic haze. My mind wandered, my head lolling back on the hard metal bar that supported the seat cushion.

Somewhere, it is dinner time. Ruby and Ben and I are at the table eating pizza. Ben pulls the pepperonis off and eats them with his fingers. He is six years old and fastidious. He won't lick his fingers. He wipes his hands on a napkin.

"Dad, which is bigger, a cell or an atom?"

"A cell is bigger."

"How many atoms could fit inside a cell?" he asks.

I want to tell him, but the number is best expressed in scientific notation. It is a quantity too large even for adults to grasp, and Ben, right on target with his psychological development, is incapable of conceiving of numbers more than a few multiples of his own age. "A million million billion," I say, hoping that sounds impressive enough.

Still chewing, he asks, "Are you still writing that science book?"

I tell him yes, it is taking a long time. I have been working on it since he was three, which causes him to raise his eyebrows in surprise.

"You write slowly," he says. "I wrote a twenty-page book today."

"Oh, you did, did you?"

Ben taught himself to read and write before he left kindergarten. It took Ruby and me by surprise when, during a long car ride, Ben exclaimed, "The sign says Montreal, one hundred thirty miles! We're almost there!" Now, at almost seven, instead of playing ball or riding his bicycle, he relaxes by writing stories about his plush toys having adventures on exotic Pacific islands.

"One minute, I'll go get it," he says.

He comes back from his room carrying a sheaf of paper stapled together into a book. The printing on the front is confident and clear. *The Uncertainty Principle*. It is a story about our Siamese cat, Erwin, unable to decide whether to poop in his box or to poop outside. Most of the pages are drawings of Erwin pooping. But one page of text reads, "He tries here. He tries there. Then he tries both places at once. Erwin is a special cat. He can poop inside and outside at the same time."

"That's a pretty profound book," I tell him. "Do you know what 'profound' means?"

"No," he says, "but did you read the dedication?"

On the back of the book, he had written, "For my dad. Because he taught me to be a scientist."

Ruby was leaning on her elbow in the bed. She clenched her jaw through a particularly painful contraction. The nurse held her hand and patted her forehead with a washcloth. This made me feel inadequate and guilty because I was the one who should care for Ruby, not some stranger. But the chair had me in a supernatural grip. I was unable to move my legs or my arms. Keeping my eyes open took enormous effort, as if the Nubain were streaming through my body, too. I was incapacitated by sloth. The attending nurse, Adele, who owned the maternity ward with her confidence and apparent omniscience, put her hand on my shoulder. Short and pretty in her hospital blues, she never hesitated or stumbled, and was quick with suggestions to help Ruby feel comfortable and relaxed. She was accustomed to dealing with husbands and had told us a few moments after we met that she grew up with six brothers, so she was not impressed by men.

"We need you to wake up now," Adele said.

Needed. The nursing staff needed me. More importantly, Ruby and the baby needed me. The feeling of relief restored my will, and I was able to push myself back into the room, into the present, where Ben was flesh, not dreams. I lifted my body out of the chair and stretched. The clock read one forty-seven.

Einstein was skeptical about entanglement. He called it *spukhafte Fernwirkung*—spooky action at a distance. At first glance, quantum entanglement seems to break several serious laws of nature, the most egregious infraction being that entangled particles appear to communicate faster than light. This challenges Einstein's theory of special relativity, which claims lightspeed is an absolute limit of the universe. Nothing, no information, no powerfully accelerated particles, not even the starship *Enterprise*, can travel faster. The amount of energy it takes to accelerate an object continues to increase as its velocity increases, so accelerating an ordinary thing like a Toyota Prius to just under the speed of light would require more energy, probably, than human beings have used since the discovery of fire. If you could survive such an experiment, sitting in that car, you would experience all manner of strange effects. As you speeded up to, say, a hundredth the speed of light (roughly five million miles an hour), you might be lucky enough to feel completely normal, but looking out the window you would see distances become shorter, and time go slower. In short, all of the natural ratios that we are accustomed to would start to flex and strain. You would, in effect, enter a new world in which distance and time had unfamiliar relationships to each other.

The man who came to give Ruby an epidural had the hands of Death, long articulated fossils that clattered against the medical cart he was pushing. He spoke to Ruby with a whisper of cold breath, his lower lip trembling as if it were afraid of the rest of his face. This was a man who liked to take people to the brink and, I surmised, usher them back with reluctance. Ruby had insisted on an epidural since ten minutes after the pregnancy test came back positive. She spoke of it with a tone of glad entitlement, and a little *schadenfreude* for the generations of women who had labored before her with nothing more than a pan of hot water and a slug of whiskey.

"Natural childbirth," she quipped, "is when you arrive at the maternity ward without any makeup."

I did not begrudge her the right to mitigate her pain. The fact that science found a way to shut down her nervous system selectively without hurting her or the child is admirable. Wonderful. But once I saw the face of the sorcerer who was going to administer the potion, I cast my eyes about the room in search of a weapon with which to disarm him. The drawer full of syringes had potential. Ruby's IV drip was suspended from a metal rack that could serve as a cudgel. To make matters worse, as he began to assemble his arcane instruments, the anesthesiologist asked me to leave. The last of my trust dissolved once he asked to work without a witness, but the formidable Adele insisted it was a good time for me to take a break. Ruby gave me a double thumbs-up to let me know she was comfortable. It was nearly three a.m., and I was aching for coffee, so I relented.

I followed the empty hallways toward the cafeteria, mumbling to myself. The cafeteria was closed but still smelled of dehydrated eggs and bacon grease. There were a few vending machines at the end of the serving area, past the row of stainless-steel steam tables and lonely pastry cases. The hot-drinks machine had a sign on it depicting an enticing, steamy cup of fresh coffee, but I knew before I put the first quarter in the slot that the liquid I was about to receive would taste like diluted potting soil. The dining area was empty except for a man in scrubs sitting at one of the tables, an unlit cigarette in his hand. I carried my paper cup to a seat two tables away from him. The coffee didn't taste like potting soil. It tasted like nothing at all, which was a good thing, because I calculated I would have to consume at least two of them to raise my caffeine level to a useful concentration. Three a.m. in a hospital basement. Above me were eighteen floors of sick people, recovering people, people giving birth, people dying. This was the nexus of human misery.

My reflection in the window was dour and rumpled. I looked older, almost twice my age. Maybe it was the cheap fluorescent lights or the hour, but when I stared into the glass, I saw the face of my father. What would he have said to me if he were here, instead of waiting for a joyous phone call back at the retirement community?

"It's not going to be easy. In some ways it'll be harder for you than it was for me. Back in my day, there were different expectations. I was just expected to do my job and support the family. I was not a 'new-age man.' I never changed a diaper or did the middle-of-the-night feedings. It was the sixties, after all. Things are different now. But you are a natural. Love comes easy to you, which at times has been your own burden.

"When you moved to Europe, I thought it was the

most selfish thing you could possibly do. I felt as if a part of me had been torn away—a limb, or a vital organ. And, like people who are missing a limb, I experienced a phantom. I could tell when you were happy and when you were lonely. When you fell in love, I knew it at once. When your heart was broken, I was troubled. A parent can feel this way about his children and still have his own inner life. Now that you're about to have your own child, everything will change. The center of your world will shift. And don't think the universe centers on him, either. It is somewhere between the three of you—you, Ruby, and this new little boy. Each of you will have your own life, but you will be entangled. It is a rare gift. Look around you and see how many of these little universes fail to coalesce. Yours will be strong because of the person you are, because of the people Ruby and your son will be."

My childhood was like this—unconditional love mixed with the smells of bourbon and cigarettes. I forgave my father long ago for his moods, his outbursts, his bigotries, as I hope my child will offer me clemency for my own. Despite the fact that most of my son's physical form comes from the pasta and cheese Ruby has eaten over the past ten months, I know the seeds of that form came from my own body. His body is not made out of my body, but his essence comes partly from my essence. Not the particle but the wave.

The lights were on in the delivery room. A nurse was at Ruby's bed, another one across the room fiddling with a high-powered standing lamp. The anesthesiologist had left, and Ruby was scowling.

Adele said, "You're going to feel the urge to push, but don't push yet. We're just getting you set up, honey, and you don't want to exhaust yourself."

Ruby took my hand. "You missed the fun," she said. "They had to take the epidural out. The shithead screwed up, and I passed out. They had to revive me with some sort of antidote."

Adele was putting the finishing touches on a saline drip in the back of Ruby's hand. "He's not one of our favorites, that one," she grumbled without looking up. The other nurse had finished her work with the spotlight and rolled it in position to shine between Ruby's legs.

"Just before I woke up," Ruby continued, "I mean, it's like my brain was just coming back from being unconscious—it was scary how completely I blacked out—and when I came back, it was like climbing out of someplace dark and cold, and I thought I had already had the baby. I really believed that it was all over. And when I woke up a little more, I couldn't feel my legs, and I didn't see any baby and you weren't here. I thought I had died. You know? I couldn't feel most of my body, and I was staring down the bed and nobody was here. I was terrified." She squeezed my hand. "Where were you?"

"I wasn't far."

In some sense she was right, though. Baby was here already. Crunched up inside her uterus, his head pushing downward toward the birth canal, he was ready to leave the comfort and safety of the wet cave that was his entire universe. If I could pick him up and carry him away from the rude lights, the heartless sterility of the hospital room, I would do so. I would spare Ruby the pain of giving birth, take her by the hand, and walk away from this place, our baby cradled in her arms. But there was no avoiding the ordeal that was to follow.

The on-call obstetrician had arrived, a woman with horn-rimmed glasses and dreadlocks. Her nametag said simply, Brice. She took my hand—not so much shaking it as holding it comfortingly—and told me where to stand. "Will you want to cut the umbilical cord?" she asked. I hadn't thought about it until then, but cutting the cord seemed too heavy with symbolism. Today was about joining the three of us as a family, not about encouraging my newborn's independence. I struggled to find a way to decline without sounding squeamish, but all I managed was "No, thanks." She took Ruby's hand, too, but not the same way. She wrapped Ruby's arm around her own waist as she sat on the bed. Brice had summed her up and knew this as the way to gain Ruby's confidence.

"Now, Ruby," she said, "I can't say this is going to be fun, but it's not going to be as horrible as you might think."

"Oh, really?" Ruby was eating it up. "Just how bad would you say it's going to be?"

"Worse than a bikini wax. Not as bad as breaking a leg."

"I can live with that," she replied, attempting a smile.

Brice came around between Ruby's legs. "Just one simple instruction. Push when I say push. Don't push when I say don't push. Okay?"

"Okay."

"Great," Brice said, putting her mask on. "Let's have a baby."

At the very instant Ruby began to push, her brother awoke in his bed three towns away, turned to his wife, and put his head close to her ear. "Ruby's having our nephew," he whispered.

Saint Gerard Majella was an Italian Catholic missionary who became the patron saint of laboring mothers. He is said to have had the power to relieve women's pain during childbirth and to be in two places at once. If I had those powers, I would have exerted them now. I would have taken Ruby's pain into my own body, and in a quantum leap to the shoreline, expelled it into the river. The fact is, I had no pain inside me at all. I didn't feel a thing. I tried the absurd thought experiments women had told me would simulate the experience: Imagine pulling your upper lip over the top of your head. Men with foreskins, imagine something similar. Imagine passing a kidney stone the size of a billiard ball. None of this imagining caused actual pain in my body. It only reinforced the fact that something was happening over there, in Ruby, that was not happening over here, inside me. There have been moments when we have experienced the world with one mind—the view of the Piazza San Marco; the miraculous pairing of a cheese from Rocamadour with a bottle of Saint-Émilion. But most of the time our interior lives are inaccessible to each other. All I could do at that moment was hold her hand and watch as she writhed and grunted. Despite how far humanity has come, how diligently we have applied ourselves to medicine and science and technology, in the most fundamental moments of our lives, we still resemble barnyard animals.

And then all at once there was light. I thought at first it was a distended section of Ruby's insides, red and speckled with tiny hairs. But it was moving outward, and Brice had her hands under it, and then it stopped being part of Ruby and became its own thing, round and miniature. It was his head.

Buried in the Earth's crust beneath the Swiss-French border, the Large Hadron Collider is revving its engines, getting ready to blast tiny hapless Hadrons to smithereens. A seventeen-mile tunnel lined with lead and kitted out with enormous electromagnets, the Large Hadron Collider is currently the largest and most expensive scientific apparatus in the world. Two beams of subatomic particles chase each other around the tunnel, accelerating near to the speed of light. When they collide somewhere on the clock face of the circle, they can create larger, more arcane particles that yield clues about the conditions at the Big Bang, the beginning of time. An experimental apparatus even more powerful than the Large Hadron Collider might one day validate a controversial idea that all of the subatomic forces derive from strands of energy that resemble strings. These strings vibrate and undulate in unimaginably complicated ways. They reach across inconceivably long distances and take shortcuts through unfamiliar dimensions. In theory, strings are smaller than any subatomic particle, yet they might keep planets in their orbits and power the stars. And so, each time we learn more about the origins of the universe, a sufficient explanation recedes by another order of magnitude. We chase it down the infinitely small, infinitely deep rabbit hole, only to find there is another infinitely small, infinitely deep rabbit hole inside.

The evidence that comes of big science experiments may reveal what the religiously faithful have been saying for centuries: we are all bound together by a single unifying force that has numerous manifestations. Energy and matter are aspects of the same thing. God is One. We are created from His raw materials, the raw materials being One. The One gives us form, substance, and duration. If entangled particles behave like One, it is because they are bound together by this unifying force. Our own bodies and souls are wrinkles in this same fabric, and our lives the result of a happy collision. We have will, yes, and individual natures. We are made of atoms just like stars and clay, and the forces that bind those atoms together bind humanity together, too.

The clock read five-thirty a.m., March 11, 2000. The beginning of the Third Millennium. Ruby was asleep, her breaths coming with deep regularity, her face the picture of abject relief. Ruby's brother had arrived with coffee and pastries. We hadn't called anyone yet, so his timing was uncanny. Baby Ben was cradled in my hand, as small as a cat and as quiet. His eyes were wide open, and though I knew he was neurologically incapable of seeing more than the shape of a nipple, I believed he was looking at me, into me. As I stared into his eyes, I lost my balance, fell into their translucent blueness, felt myself swept into a tight vortex prescribed by three points:

Ruby in the bed sleeping, baby Ben in my arms looking up at me, my own face staring down at myself. I was a proton unleashed, flying in circles through a magnetic field, rotating with the axis of the Earth, orbiting the spinning Sun as it continued its Ferris-wheel tour of creation.

WAVE-
PARTICLE
DUALITY

When we wake up brushed by panic in the dark
our pupils grope for the shape of things we know.

Photons loosed from slits like greyhounds at the track
reveal light's doubleness in their cast shadows

that stripe a dimmed lab's wall—particles no more—
and with a wave bid all certainties goodbye.
      —Sarah Howe, "Relativity (for Stephen Hawking)"

THE NAKED WOMAN REACHES TOWARD ME, HER ARMS AND LEGS SPREAD OPEN, A COME-HITHER TWINKLE IN HER EYES. Now I am touching her breasts, now furtively reaching between her thighs. She touches me there, and there, and—oh, yes—right there. My breath comes quicker and deeper as our bodies entwine. I can feel her heat close around me. Her name is Tiffany, and she likes hiking, shopping, and ice cream. This is the third time the twenty-one-year-old and I have made love this year, and with any luck today will be the last. As I drop the magazine and reach for the specimen cup, I wonder if my child is going to look like Miss November.

The average human ejaculate contains about 5ml of liquid and ninety million sperm. A nation in a teaspoon. With tens of millions of sperm descending on a single egg, conception ought to be a simple matter of boys meet girl. But in my case, something had gone wrong. A lab technician confirmed it: 5ml of my stuff only contained a city-bus-full of sperm, and almost half of them swam in circles, chasing their tails like demented kittens. A large number of them had no heads at all. They were just wriggling commas completely useless as fertilization material.

When I first had the analysis done, I couldn't help but take the technician's comments personally. I was embarrassed at the various deformities she described, as if they were an expression of my own inadequacy. This was, after all, my personal genetic material we were talking about. It wasn't just my virility that was being measured, but my capacity to reproduce and, thus, my usefulness as a human being.

In the days when Ruby and I were younger and more fertile, we conceived Ben with good timing and some sterile instruments other than my own. To perform this act, we invited a stranger dressed as a nurse to inject sperm into my wife. While this might seem like the post-modern version of a swinging threesome, the purpose of intrauterine insemination was to bypass the messy, pleasurable, biological stuff and get right to the point. Unlike sex, the experience began with the man producing the ejaculate. This was transferred to the back rooms of the fertility clinic where it was analyzed and centrifuged, and nonessential compounds like attraction, love, and pleasure were removed. A little while later, the nurse arrived in the exam room carrying a tiny vial of transparent, pink fluid. In a few well-practiced gestures, she positioned her head between my wife's legs, sucked the juice out of the bottle with a catheter, thrust it deep inside, then asked *me* to squeeze the handle, so it squirted into Ruby's uterus. I always do as I'm told when it comes to my wife and medical instruments sticking out of her body, but I never saw the point in this part of the exercise. The nurse should have finished the job herself. Ruby was put off, too. But as I pushed the fluid out of the catheter and mocked, "Ooh, baby," Ruby cracked a smile. That was it. The nurse withdrew the catheter, shook our hands, and left. Ten minutes later, we were in the parking lot drinking weak coffee out of Styrofoam cups.

We repeated this kinky role-playing game six times, until the egg and sperm got the steps to the fertility dance right, and Ruby started to grow a healthy boy-fetus.

Three years had intervened, and our bodies had become even less fit for reproduction. The doctor was right to prescribe the mother of all infertility treatments: In-Vitro Fertilization. In our condition, with my brain-damaged sperm and Ruby's unstable endocrine system, we were unlikely to conceive without the reproductive equivalent of the Manhattan Project. So once again, I found myself producing the euphemistically misnamed "sample."

This experience is not so fun as it may sound. It is

sometimes stressful, usually clinical, and always humiliating. I had the option of doing it at home, as long as I could get the stuff to the clinic within thirty minutes. I have always subscribed to the philosophy, however, that it is best to transport your body fluids within your own body, so they will be at their freshest when they are dispensed. For those who have religious objections or are simply too squeamish to masturbate, the option of last resort is to undergo a procedure that will cause your body to expectorate semen forcibly. This is exactly what farmers do with prize cattle, and it involves electrical probes and desecrations far exceeding the embarrassment of a little jerking off. It is hard to imagine that anyone would volunteer for such humiliation, unless he misinterpreted the written instructions, which say, "If you wish, a nurse can assist you to extract the sample." Ruby was in another wing of the hospital getting prepped for egg retrieval. All I had to do was hide in a closet and spank my monkey. I'd been practicing for this moment since I was thirteen.

Getting sperm out of an average human male is as easy as starting a car. Getting the eggs out of a woman's ovaries, however, is an invasive surgical procedure that requires anesthetic, a surgical team, and an operating theater. First the woman is knocked out, so she will lie still. She is hooked up to a heart monitor, oxygen, and saline drip. The doctor passes a tube up her vaginal canal, poking it through her cervix, then into her uterus, and finally into a fallopian tube where, using gentle suction, it pops the eggs into its mouth like berries. The pipette is withdrawn, the egg placed in a set of Petri dishes, and the woman unhooked. Then the doctor washes up and thanks God she conceived her own children the easy way.

The medical team watches the progress of the tube on a television monitor, the images being supplied by ultrasound, so nobody but the anesthesiologist actually looks at the woman. There is no need. At this moment, she is no more than a carton of eggs. It is important for the doctors and technicians to maintain an emotional distance from the patient. Nothing less than complete dehumanization can keep them from crumpling with anxiety when committing surgery on a human body. While lying on the operating table, a woman is a complicated biological system in need of repair. When she opens her eyes and speaks, she's a human being again. Technology and a technological perspective allow us to concentrate on the physical nature of a person and ignore her humanity.

This is what it is like to be a medical professional— now treating a body as a biological artifact, now talking to her as a human being with feelings. One does not have to be a doctor to confront this kind of duality. Anyone who eats meat knows this. It is easy to pet a sheep, look into its eyes, and see consciousness there, then tuck into a satisfying dinner of lamb stew. Recognizing duality means stripping away meaning, trying to see a familiar thing out of its normal context. A foreign language sounds like a jumble of sound until one acquires the skill to recognize individual words. Under certain circumstances, even one's mother tongue can sound like haphazard grunts and mumbles.

We settled into a private hospital room for Ruby's procedure preparation. She was probed and measured and poked with countless needles, cords, and hoses, then given a mild sedative. She had not eaten or drunk anything for fourteen hours, and by the time we arrived she'd already entered a hypoglycemic haze. We spent the morning navigating periods of boredom punctuated by bursts of activity. From time to time a technician came to take her blood pressure, adjust an intravenous needle, administer an antibiotic. Ruby rested uncomfortably on a gurney, wearing a ridiculous hospital gown that provided as much modesty as a yarmulke, trying hard to engage herself in a *People* magazine. I paced about, wishing for coffee, but knowing that the smell of it would make her crazy. Seeing her hooked up to a heart monitor and an intravenous drip, I felt I should say something profound. A declaration of love seemed redundant, because she knew I wouldn't have put up with this ordeal and all of the concomitant crap if I didn't love her. We made weak jokes, small talk, snide observations about the hospital staff while the clock ticked ever more slowly toward the moment when I was called away to my peculiar task, and she was taken under by the drugs into unconsciousness.

Time does not unravel at a constant rate for everybody. Time is as subjective as color, or the way we perceive ourselves and each other. It is a fundamental tenet of the universe that time passes differently for objects in separate frames of reference. A body moving at a velocity close to the speed of light gets older at a slower rate than a body at rest. The faster you travel away from me, the slower your clock will go as compared with mine. If one morning you were to rocket into space at very near the speed of light and come back when your spaceship's clock said it was time for lunch, I would be long dead. The reason for this is counterintuitive but logical: the speed of light is the same for everyone, no matter how fast you are moving. Inside your speeding rocket, you see the light from the Sun traveling at 186,000 miles per second. The same light reaches me, sitting quietly in a deck chair by the pool, at exactly the same velocity. The speed of light is a cosmic constant, and time, space, causality, and simultaneity are subordinate to that.

Ruby was about to skip across the next three hours like a stone skipping across the surface of a lake. Once the anesthetic took effect, her timeline folded over on itself. She pushed through the fold, emerging on the other side unaware that she had grown three hours older, whereas I had gone the long way around, earthbound, lumbering along at our old familiar pace.

What was it like for Ruby? Did she dream of eggs and sperm dancing about, the eggs wearing tutus, each sperm in a single tap shoe? Or enormous families of nineteen children emanating from her uterus in a reenactment of the Gaia story, infants and children sucking at her breasts? She may not have had a chance to dream at all. She might have stared up at the benevolent face of the anesthetist and obediently counted backward from ninety-nine by sevens (*ninety-nine, ninety-two, eighty-five, seventy-nine—no eight, . . . seventy-one . . . sev*). A black millisecond later, she will awake in the recovery room with a mouth as dry as paper, feeling like she's been on a bender. She may experience soreness, or a horrific residual memory of being probed by an alien instrument. If she tries, she can dismiss these as Freudian imagery or a nightmare influenced by recent television programs about UFOs. Anyone who has been put under will tell you it's not like sleeping. It is disturbingly close to death, or at least the closest thing to death that living people can imagine. It is not a state from which you awaken. Instead, you return to consciousness realizing that you have climbed out of a bottomless pit. *Then* you fall asleep.

I am ushered to a small and cozy room. The walls and floor are a tasteful, subdued peach. A leatherette sofa is aligned along a wall. Facing it, a framed print of a naked woman lying on her belly, propped on her arms, reading a book, her position chosen to amplify the curves of her buttocks and breasts. The juxtaposition of propriety and nakedness is what makes the picture naughty. A white-noise machine exhales watery sounds from a table in the corner. Next to it, a stack of clean towels. At the other end of the room is a standard industrial bathroom—clean enough to eat in and entirely unremarkable save for a tiny trapdoor in the wall above the toilet, which opens to reveal a tiny shelf, and another tiny door on the other side of the wall. When I finish, I am supposed to place the specimen cup and paperwork in that peep-show contraption, close the door on my side, and flip a switch to tell the technician the sample is ready.

I turn my attention to the coffee table in front of the sofa. The furniture is appropriate for a family room, which seems absurd, since I am about to do something that is definitely not family-friendly. On the table, I find a specimen cup, some forms to be filled out, and a pile of magazines. The forms are a drag, and I get them out of the way as quickly as possible, so I can see what kind of erotica the clinic provided. Like most men, I get turned on by the sight of beautiful young women frolicking in the nude. The fact that I generate fewer sperm than most men doesn't seem to make a difference. I've long been a fan of middle-of-the-road pornography—nothing deviant or creepy, just pictures of people touching each other in ways you don't see at Starbucks. I pass no judgment, as long as nobody gets hurt. For me, looking at *Penthouse* is a guilty vicarious thrill, like watching Jacques Pépin prepare a *génoise*, or inhaling secondhand smoke from a high-quality cigar. None of these is as good as the real thing. Then again, the real thing isn't always that good, either. The dessert on TV was prepared in a hurry under hot lights. The woman in the triple-X video enjoying herself by the pool doesn't moan like that when she's off duty. Maybe she giggles insipidly or can't get her tongue around the word "nuclear," both of which would be significant turnoffs. Vicarious titillation only works when it is far removed from reality and nourished with plenty of imagination.

Judging by the magazines on the coffee table, it is clear that they hired the wrong person to do the dirty shopping. Whoever supplied this room with *Juggs*, *Cosmopolitan*, and the Iraq issue of *Playboy* had no idea what makes men click. This is a desperate situation. Men come in here keyed up. We need some serious, uncensored help. I scan the *Playboy* looking for pictures that would get my mind off the things that could go wrong—impotence and spillage being the main ones—and put me in a more salubrious frame of mind. It is disastrously counterproductive when I open the magazine to a full-page photo of Saddam Hussein. Even now, in my imagination, I hear him challenging me with his smug, mustachioed grin. "Just try to get it up now, you slack American weenie." My warhead remained disarmed.

A suitably exciting centerfold would help to dispel that horrible image. And there she is. Wearing nothing but a pair of earrings, relaxing on a pink divan, fingering a book with one hand and her vagina with the other. A quick zip should suffice, but something might get caught. I glance around the room nervously, not entirely convinced that there is not a camera or a one-way mirror installed for some federally justified government purpose. I remove my shoes and pull down my pants. Flipping through the magazines, I lie on the sofa, twisted inside-out with guilt and revulsion. I try to derive enough pleasure to accomplish the task at hand without actually enjoying myself.

Upstairs in the operating room, Ruby's body is being probed with sharp instruments. Simultaneously, my body experiences an orgasm.

Peering into the little plastic cup before placing it into the trapdoor, I think: somewhere in that opaque drop of Elmer's glue is a speck, just one among tens of millions blindly jostling and bravely striving forward and upward toward an egg that is, at the moment, a few yards down the hall. I could choose to look at the sample in several different ways. A vile bodily secretion that should never be seen or discussed in public. A beautiful sacred potion that can create life. A DNA concentrate. The key to the continuation of the species. More specifically, the key to the resuscitation of my family tree. A fluid that transports the past into the future. Semen is liquid information.

A single spermatozoon carries half of the genetic information necessary to make a human being. It is the sum of wisdom passed along by my parents and grandparents. (My grandmother's contributions were "Wear a hat when it is cold," and "When you make chicken soup, be sure to add a little dill if you have it.") A single cell contains the memories of all the generations preceding me, and the evolutionary knowledge that will make it possible for my child to breathe oxygenated air, to digest tomatoes, to use language, to fight disease. We are part of a larger organism that exists to propagate DNA.

When considered this way, the gob of spunk in a cup is a glance through a temporal lens. Not this individual, me, but this moment in a wave that began when life began and spread over the earth.

Is duality merely a quality of human thought? Our brains evidently are wired to see things two ways. Our visual cortex can be fooled by simple drawings such as the Duck/Rabbit:

and the Old Woman/Young Woman:

Is it a duck? Yes. It is also a rabbit. One can choose to see it either way. The meaning changes as soon as we make the decision. The meaning is not inherent in the drawing itself. It congeals only when we choose to observe it. A wave function collapsing to a particle.

Nature does a fan-dance with reality: now seducing us to believe that atoms are little balls you can cup in your hand, now concealing their weight when we reach out to hold them, now hinting that they were waves all along, now lifting the veil on even more complex behaviors. She performs a little magic here and there, flirting with us until we discover the next truth in a long line of truths that seem to contradict each other. Modern physicists believe that when these persistent dualities converge, they will see and understand the secrets of the universe.

It is no coincidence that the discovery of quantum uncertainty and wave-particle duality, which entered the public consciousness in the early 1900s, coincided with movements in art and philosophy that called into question the very meaning of meaning. Dada artist Marcel Duchamp's *In Advance of a Broken Arm* (a shovel, 1915) and *Fountain* (a urinal, 1917) are not statements that art has no meaning, but that *meaning* itself is a subjective term. (When is one forbidden to use the toilet at a museum? When the toilet is the exhibit.) Kurt Schwitters, well known for his Dadaist paintings, also wrote Dadaist poetry. One amusing ditty, called *Wand* (Wall), consists of thirty-seven repetitions of the word *Wand*. Schwitters meant the poem to be read aloud. Repeating any word more than ten times will surely rinse away any residual meaning. The mind disengages. All that is left is a wave pattern traveling between peoples' heads. The word is still a word, but it is also just a sound as insignificant as the rustling of leaves or a cow saying *moo*.

Ruby is in the recovery room now, one of six unconscious women in a neat row lined up like salamis.

Several nurses sit around a small desk filing paperwork, waiting for signs of life. Somebody stirs, and a nurse ambles to the bedside, takes the woman's hand, and slaps it—harder than a "there, there," but not hard enough to raise a rash.

"Diane. Diane, honey," she says, "can you hear me?"

The salami mumbles something unintelligible to normal human ears. It sounds like "Glurh."

The nurse, however, accustomed to the language of the near-dead, responds, "It hurts? We'll get you something. Here, Diane, try to drink."

The nurse puts a straw in a cup of water and shoves the straw into the woman's mouth. Nothing. Then, a slight wrinkling of her brow, an immeasurably small lowering of the water level in the cup.

"That's good, Diane. Now, you rest. We'll give you something for the pain."

A healthy thirty-something woman can return from the Underworld in about forty-five minutes. Ruby has half an hour to go.

In the next room, the surgical team hovers over a gurney. The patient starts to count backward from ninety-seven by threes. Outside in the parking lot, I lean against our car, squinting against the glare from nearby windshields. I watch a couple leave the hospital, the woman on the man's arm, a little wobbly, looking pale and exhausted. Upstairs in a laboratory, my chromosomes are about to converge with Ruby's through a technique with the lyrical name Intracytoplasmic Sperm Injection.

Applying the powers vested in him by the Massachusetts Institute of Technology, the lab-coated technician manually joins the two cells together in holy conception. Using instruments so small only a robotic arm could grasp them, he gently cracks one of Ruby's eggs and goes fishing in a vial of sperm. He peers down the tube of a microscope, watching the sperm as they swim about, until one pops to the surface. He yanks gently and pulls it out of the vial, its tail wriggling, struggling to get free. Does it know it only has thirty minutes to live? Would it prefer to die in that primordial pond with its blind brothers, or after weeks of yearning, to be guided by an immortal hand to Egg—that benevolent Zion of which a sperm can only dream—where it will find blessed transubstantiation?

Egg is near. He cannot see her, but he can feel her. A thousand times his size, he is drawn by her gravitational pull, feels its tug at every molecule, enticing him, needing him, giving his puny life a purpose before she takes it from him entirely. Once inside, there are a few moments of calm during which nothing happens at all. A brief pause while the universe recalculates the order of the generations. Then the sperm notices his molecules and atoms being torn from him, floating away to join with her. But wait, is he being torn apart particle by particle, or is he resonating with her, their frequencies converging first in dissonance, then in subatomic harmony? As he loses his edges, his substance dissipates, his own wave function collapses, and he becomes an integral variable in hers. She is singing gently to him, holding him tight and crooning a palliative song of conception to accompany his decay to a complex tensor function. It is a low, rhythmic thrumming that emanates from every protein, every strand of RNA that unzips his chromosomes and zips them up with hers. It is the background noise of the cosmos revealing itself to him in his last moments in the universe. It is saying, *Wand. Wand. Wand.*

COLD
FUSION

long is the way
And hard, that out of Hell leads up to Light;
—John Milton, *Paradise Lost*

HAVE JUST RETURNED FROM WORK. Ruby is at the counter cutting vegetables. The sink is full of dirty dishes, and the floor is an obstacle course of laundry and toys. Ben clambers down the stairs with a million things to tell me. He is talking in rapid enthusiastic phrases. "We went swimming and you know what I got a car and you know what kind it is it is a—you won't believe this—it is a Buick and you know what else Mama and me went to the bank and there was a dog there and he had big lips."

Ruby is cranky. She is trying to prepare dinner for us, and nothing is working out. "I thought we had eggs, but they expired. I'm having to make do with what was in the freezer. And look at this." She puts down the knife and opens the refrigerator to take out a bottle of seltzer. "Is there a reason you put this back in the fridge?" She shakes the bottle at me, and I can see about an inch of water sloshing at the bottom. "Really. Please tell me what I'm supposed to do with this?"

I open my mouth to answer. If she had discovered the bottle while I was there, it would have made sense for her to get annoyed. But keeping it in the fridge to show me when I came home was an act of spite.

Before I can compose my thoughts, she barks, "Answer me. I asked you a question."

"I'm sorry," I start, thinking I can change her mood by being contrite. This is my first mistake.

"Don't tell me you're sorry," she snaps. "Sorry does not mean anything. I've told you that before. Sorry is what you say when you're trying to brush me off. You're not going to brush me off. You did something stupid, and you have to admit it." She shoves the bottle to my chest. "Get rid of this."

"Come on, buddy," I say to Ben, "let's go to your room

to see your books."

Ben takes my hand, and we amble back to his room at a three-year-old pace. I can hear Ruby banging pots in the kitchen.

According to some experimenters, one can run a steady current through a sliver of palladium suspended in a mason jar of heavy water, and after a few weeks the system will start putting out more energy than you put in. It will come out in the form of heat—a slow burn that may last a month. Nobody is certain why this happens. The people who claim to have observed this behavior call it "cold fusion." They surmise that free electrons in the heavy water get bound up with the atomic lattice of the palladium and cause the nuclei to fuse. Conventional scientists have proposed it is simply a buildup of volatile gases in the heavy water that steadily combust. People have been conducting experiments in cold fusion for thirty years but have yet to prove that it is a nuclear phenomenon. The scientific community at large scoffs at the subject. The party line is that you can't get more energy out of a system than you put into it.

Most respected scientists liken cold fusion claims to assertions of perpetual motion and classify its proponents as cranks or fools. The scientific community rejects it out of hand, not only because it challenges established dogma, but because the people who discovered it did not follow the standard procedures for bringing their discovery to the attention of the scientific world. For a group that prides itself on the checks and balances of repeatable experimentation and peer-review, this was apostasy. For this reason, the only people who are willing to conduct cold-fusion experiments are scientists at the end of their careers with nothing to lose. No graduate student or young professor with aspirations to tenure will mention the subject. Today, a few dozen scientists around the world work in secret to prove that cold fusion is real. If it is, it could save the world by providing an endless source of energy. If it is fantasy, then at least it is a fantasy based on hope.

Ruby has been injecting herself with a steady dose of follicle-stimulating hormone for three weeks. It has built up inside her bloodstream and activated her ovaries, which, in turn, began to churn out chemicals of their own: estradiol, luteinizing hormone, estrogen. The extra FSH is intended to make her generate dozens of viable eggs that the doctors can harvest and fertilize. During this phase of her cycle, Ruby goes in for regular ultrasound exams to track her progress. Her last exam showed that she is incubating a chicken-coopful of eggs, each one encased in a juicy ovarian follicle. They are clumped together like tapioca, a couple of millimeters round. But the drugs she is taking are psychoactive. She is more than simply irritable. She is prone to fulminant rages.

Ben is settled in my lap with a copy of *Green Eggs and Ham*. He is blissfully oblivious to the tension between his mother and me, and I try to hide my own growing anxiety. When she is in this state, she will not bear being challenged; yet she despises any sign of passivity, any indication that I am trying to avoid a conflict. She is a Kamikaze on her final dive toward her target, and no amount of reason or compassion or pleading or anger will stop her. Her blood is burning, her internal organs have turned to hot rocks, and she needs release.

Ruby gets worked up to this state easily these days. She starts the day at peace but, sometime after the morning round of shots, the pressure starts building, her voice grows strained, and she loses her usual fluidity of motion. It starts with her frustration with ordinary things—a recalcitrant jar of pasta sauce, an obstinate shirt button—until she reaches a tipping point that launches her into an ecstatic state. She comes undone like a person in a sexual frenzy or the throes of a spiritual epiphany. For Ruby, who is naturally methodical, these episodes are bewildering, and the comedown is sometimes just as bad. She returns to her normal self, exhausted and depressed.

I am not nearly as emotionally limber as she. I have spent most of my life in the mid-range. Rarely voluble, I have a habit of suppressing anger. But when I do get worked up into a lather, I whine like an old vacuum cleaner. This difference is physical, like the difference between our faces, or the fact that Ruby can put the palms of her hands on the floor without bending her knees, whereas I can barely reach into my pockets. It appears to me that her volatile state is a quality of her wanting. It seems to go deeper than her intellect, deeper than anything she may be conscious of. Maybe this is the way every cell in her body, every strand of DNA, cries out to be pregnant again. Under ordinary circumstances, she may be able to suppress these cries, to push down against the pressure of her cells. But the drugs have worn her adult superego down to a nub, returning her to a vulnerable childhood without the capacity to integrate her inner life with the life outside her body. Does she hear, taste, feel everything in her life with the same intensity? That pain must be unbearable.

The people who pursue cold fusion do it with irrational fervor, unable to concentrate on subjects within the confines of modern scientific practice. They are driven by the idea of something larger and more important than themselves. They spend their careers quite literally out of control, carried on the wave crests of their wanting. A zealot doesn't think about what he is sacrificing for his cause. The cause chooses him. Like the *Übermensch*, Nietzsche's *Zarathustra*, a zealot "goes under," relinquishing every connection with the ordinary plane of the world so he can slip below and reshape it for his own ends. Indeed, everything that has transpired on this day is a result of Ruby and me being consumed by our desire for another child.

The original cold-fusion experiments were crude setups involving sealed mason jars and vacuum pumps. The assemblies sat in the corners of laboratories designed for other reasons—usually labs devoted to nuclear chemistry or low-energy physics. Some of the scientists who assisted with these experiments were graduate students in their twenties working toward their masters or PhDs, bleary-eyed from lack of sleep, jittery from excess caffeine, and probably bored. The experiments took a day or two to assemble and initialize, then sat around for weeks producing no observable results. On any given morning, a grad student might walk into the lab, quickly glance at the computer screen attached to the gear, and sigh when nothing had changed. Perhaps he would lean in toward the glass of the mason jar, tap it a little with the back of a finger in the manner of someone kicking the tires of a car—a meaningless gesture that produces no useful information, but makes a person feel better about not knowing what is going on inside. Then he would go on about his day.

One such morning in 1992, a cold-fusion researcher named Michael McKubre entered the lab at Stanford Research Institute in Menlo Park, California. The mason jar had filled with hot, combustible gases overnight and was just waiting to be provoked. Maybe he tapped on the glass. Maybe he dropped something onto the lab bench. There was a loud pop like a gun going off. Shards of glass flew about the room, crashing into lab equipment and slicing the graduate student's skin. The hot gases combusted and released even more heat, melting the palladium, superheating the heavy water, reducing the entire experiment to a gooey mass. When the dust settled, McKubre was bleeding from wounds that would leave permanent scars. The man who had been standing next to him was dead.

I hear a loud clattering from the kitchen. "Shit!" Ruby yells. When I run in, she is standing over a blood-red mess. She has dropped a jar of tomato sauce. I grab a sponge and crouch down. "Don't touch it!" Her voice stops me in mid-reach. "Why the hell am I the one preparing dinner? Why don't you make dinner some time? I hate having to do all of the cooking!" She is really screaming now. Her hands are clenched tightly, her arms down at her sides.

"You're right," I say. "You should take a break. Let me clean this up, and I'll take care of the rest of dinner."

"Back off!" It is more of a warning than a threat. She can tell that she has reached a point of irreversible volatility. Childish, irrational, superheated with fury. She is helpless.

Foolishly, I move forward to calm her. She grabs a pan from the top of the stove and throws it down, splattering a hot mess over my legs and arms. She leans in toward my face and spits, "Bastard! Don't come near me. You are selfish and stupid and weak, and I hate you." She runs down the stairs and slams the door.

Now she is releasing the energy. It comes out in the form of heat that could melt my skin. The house is aflame with her rage. Ben is at the door of the kitchen. His anguished face is wet from his tears. He is crying so hard he cannot make a sound, and his small, vulnerable body is quivering. I lean down and take him in my arms. His clothes are drenched from sweat. I count the seconds before he is able to take a breath. Fifteen. Thirty. Forty seconds. He gasps and shudders, then starts to cry outright. He finds my ear and grabs onto it, his nails digging into my flesh. It feels like he will rip it off, but I just hold him more tightly. I cannot think of anything to say, except quietly cooing, "Shh. Shh. It's okay, honey. It's okay." I say it over and over, rhythmically, hoping it will calm him but all the time wondering if we have inflicted permanent damage on his psyche. Will he remember this day with dread when he is an adult? Will it make him an introvert? Afraid of intimacy? Unable to express anger? I already regret how this event might shape him.

The concoction of hormones Ruby has taken seems to be specially formulated to provoke the worst reactions in both of us. It produced an uncharacteristic level of aggression in Ruby. Since I never developed an adult's capacity to cope with anger, I came up with a handy set of tools to avoid conflict wherever possible. But in her state, Ruby drives a ten-ton truck of rage through my paper wall without a thought.

It was not supposed to be this way. We had dreamed of a house full of music and love. We had imagined Ben feeling safe and content in the arms of his brothers and sisters. We wanted to give our children the best of our own childhoods and avoid the failings of our parents. We thought by having children we could travel back in time and correct the past. In the pursuit of perfection, we will inevitably make our own mistakes, inflict our own special kind of damage. We can spend our lives trying to undo the errors of our pasts, but in so doing we must commit other errors—the laws of physics demand it because entropy increases—and anyway, it would be a waste of time. Too many hearts have been broken. Too many variables intervene. Now the house is burning, and McKubre's partner is dead, and we are caught in a vortex of despair. Our Faustian struggle against nature, our attempt to cheat infertility, is being met with a petulant and bitter opposing force that is intent upon breaking us.

When I look up from Ben, Ruby is standing in front of me, trembling. She looks exhausted and defeated.

"Ruby," I say, "I hate what IVF is doing to you. To us. We need to stop."

Her voice is quieter now, but it has an unfamiliar quality to it, a timbre that is deep and throaty and definitely not her own. If we were living in the seventeenth century, I would say she had been possessed by a demon. "You have no right to say that. I'm the one driving to the clinic in the morning. I'm the one taking the shots. I'm the one who has to endure the hot flashes, the pain, the bullshit. It's my body that's being abused for the sake of giving you a child. How dare you even *think* that you have anything to say about it. If you don't want children, then get the hell out of my way."

"Of course I want more children," I say, failing to keep the desperation out of my voice. Ben is old enough to understand. We are scarring him for certain. "But we have to measure the cost. Is it worth this agony? Do you see what it is doing to us? To Ben?"

"Ben's fine. You're the problem."

"No, Ruby. Right now, you're the problem."

She takes Ben in her arms, gently smoothing his hair, kissing his cheek. Too quietly she says, "Get out of the house. Now. I need you away from me."

"You're kicking me out?" I ask stupidly. "Don't do that. Let's sit quietly for a while. I'll go into the other room. Let you pull yourself together."

She is holding Ben close now. He clings to her, not sure exactly what to expect. Ruby mouths the words "fuck you" over his head so he can't see, then takes him into his room.

The argument had come with surprising swiftness, and just as quickly I am in the silence of the car. I sit in the driver's seat, staring through the windshield at the back wall of the garage. These days I am rarely alone. I awaken when Ben cries out from his bed, spend the first few minutes of the morning with him until Ruby wakes and joins us. Later, I insinuate my body into the crowded subway car, wait in line at the coffee shop, avoid the eyes of people on the elevator up to my office. At work, I spend the day in meetings, occasionally slipping out to have a quiet moment to myself. I'll go to the bathroom. Inevitably, one of the geeky guys from the meeting will appear at the latrine next to mine and strike up a dialog as he unzips. When the workday is over, I reverse the process, arriving home tense and smelling like a subway platform. The horror of modern life dissolves as I sink into the cocoon of my family. At bedtime, I cuddle up with Ben until the soft, rhythmic whistle from his tiny nose tells me he is asleep.

In the driver's seat, my heart is still pounding. I wonder if I should really go away as she asked, or if I should wait a few minutes for her to find herself again, enter the house confidently and without trace of apology, and offer her a safe shoulder? In the car with the doors closed and radio off, I experience silence and aloneness like they are new sensations. I am an individual again, not part of a pod. A sack of flesh and thoughts pressed into a bucket seat. This is the blessed silence of being alone. But there is an unpleasant quality to this silence, too. It is the horrifying quiet of the first seconds after an earthquake, when the sound like a freight train exploding through your bedroom has gone, and the shaking has stopped, and everything is still, except for the light tinkle of settling glass, and a high-pitched sound easily mistaken for something mechanical, until you realize it is your own voice keening through clenched teeth. I am caught in an uncertain moment, wondering if Ruby and I will weather this argument, or if we have been swept up in something beyond our control that will carry us beyond remediation. Her lighthearted wit has turned to scathing. Her charm has turned to belligerence. Every bright and clever thing for which I married her has become toxic. The air around her shimmers with acidic resentment. I hate what my day has become.

The keyring sits lightly in my hand. It would take no effort at all to place it in the ignition and depart forever. I am Schrödinger's cat on the brink. My mind needs only the smallest, barely measurable shove in one direction or another. A quantum hiccup in the cerebellum, perhaps unleashed by a misguided cosmic ray, and the cascade of firing neurons will spread out in all directions —the visual cortex registering the keyring, the motor cortex choreographing the actions of a hundred muscle groups as they flex and extend just so—until the key is in the ignition, and my foot is on the pedal. A quick turn to the right is all it will take. The moment that thought arrives, I know leaving would not be an act of self-defense. It would be cowardice. However trying Ruby's actions are at this instant, they are unequal to the unbearable permanent emptiness of leaving her behind.

When I return to the house, it is dark and quiet. Ruby is in Ben's room, lying on his bed with her arms around him. He is in his polar-bear pajamas. She is still dressed. The rest of the house is an inhospitable mess, but now is not the time to start rattling around to clean up. I step lightly upstairs to my bed, take off my jeans, and turn out the light. I lie there awake. My eyes refuse to close. They stare blindly into the darkness. I hear my pulse beat twice to each tick of my bedside alarm clock. I wonder if Ruby will sleep through until morning or if I face an interminable night of acrimony. After a few minutes, maybe an hour, Ruby comes up the stairs. She undresses and slips into bed. She shifts toward me, puts her arm over my waist, her leg over my leg. I feel her tremble and sigh.

The morning comes quickly.

THE
UNCERTAINTY
PRINCIPLE

Agnus Dei, qui tollis peccata mundi.
Dona nobis pacem.

"**I**'M PREGNANT."

The words hang in the air. They catch me off guard. I have grown so accustomed to the frequent visits to the clinic, the injections, the emotional volatility, the long series of disappointments, that those things have taken on a life of their own. My expectation that anything would come of them has diminished. It is as if we had simply taken on a new hobby—one that involves painful and humiliating medical procedures that have no connection to conceiving a child. My body reacts before my mind does, delivering that pinprick of adrenaline after receiving news that changes one's life.

Three years earlier, when Ruby received the positive results about Ben, she asked me to come home from work early without telling me why. She used an urgent tone that made me think our last attempt at IUI had failed. When I arrived, she put a paper hat on my head. She had decorated the apartment with streamers and confetti. She had put a birthday cake on the kitchen table with pink frosting letters that spelled out a date nine months in the future. We celebrated by dancing.

Her demeanor is very different today. She pulls me into a corner of the house where our three-year-old won't hear us. She whispers the news dully, as if it were just another complication of our strange medical fetish. When I reach out to embrace her, she stops me. "The doc says the numbers are off. It might not stick." She looks pale and frightened, the way a person does when she learns she has a serious disease. "We just need to wait, is all. I'll go in for another test in a few weeks." Then, with an exasperated sigh, "More waiting."

Earlier that day, just before dawn, Ruby unfolded herself from a restless night and got dressed. She made a pot of coffee and gathered her things while it was brewing. Wallet, keys, Filofax, insurance card. She put on a heavy parka, a wool hat, and gloves, poured her coffee into a travel mug, and stepped into the cold morning without waking our son. The drive to the clinic was swift but tedious, most of it along an empty highway. She parked in the no-stopping zone in front of the main building and set the blinkers going. She knew that at six a.m., nobody would be around to check on the car, and she would be in and out of the clinic before anyone noticed. A cheery phlebotomist ushered her to a chair. A few moments later, 2ml of her blood dripped into a test tube. Ruby had arrived early, so she could find out early. After six weeks of injections, examinations, emotional surges, she was unwilling to wait any longer than necessary for the results of a pregnancy test.

Now, we are sitting in a corner of our house wondering what to do with the information. The results are technically positive, but somewhere in the impossibly complicated recipe of chemicals that should support her pregnancy, her body has gotten the magic baby-making formula wrong. Critical supplies of human chorionic gonadotropin and progesterone, normally present in small amounts in her bloodstream, should have soared into the hundreds and thousands of parts per million. With too little progesterone, the embryo would lose its ability to multiply (One-twenty-eight, two-fifty-six . . . uh, five-eleven . . . teen) and eventually stop. Ruby's body would detect the moribund pimple on her uterus and flush it with her next menstrual period. There is no way to look inside her to determine if she is actually growing a fetus. In many ways, her body is reacting as if it were, but the only measurements that can be taken are chemical ones that imply a pregnancy, but do not prove it. Ruby is "sort of pregnant."

Once again, I am reminded of Schrödinger's cat. The original experiment was designed to illustrate the superposition of two distinct possibilities—the cat is dead *and* alive. Either outcome could be true until you open the box and observe the result. How does this conflicting pair of realities congeal into a single truth? This question is known as the "measurement problem." It is impossible to peek inside the box to see how the cat is doing, because the act of peeking terminates the experiment. Schrödinger's intent was to describe the states of subatomic particles, but his thought experiment illustrates how truth itself, the empirical idea of truth, may not exist at all. According to Heisenberg, we cannot know the momentum and position of a subatomic particle simultaneously. As soon as you measure the momentum, you affect the position. Measure its precise position, and the momentum value becomes meaningless.

When confronted with facts that are true but that contradict each other, we may assert two opposing viewpoints—that a single truth exists, and we have simply failed to measure it adequately; or that there are many potential truths until particles interact and the universe is forced to choose. Physicists reject the first viewpoint because of the neat and elegant mathematical formalism that has led them to the current conclusions. Saying "there must be some mistake" would call for the wholesale unwinding of all of modern physics back to Niels Bohr and Max Planck. To assert a multiplicity of truths seems counterintuitive, at least to minds raised in the twentieth century. To us, truth is a point on a graph. It is an incontrovertible, declarative statement: water freezes at zero degrees Celsius; London is the capital of England. Certainly, these things are so. And it would be convenient if our understanding of the world were made up of discrete blocks of truth. The fundamental tenet of science and scientific method is to build truth upon truth like a child's tower of blocks. This is what it means to know something: we observe and measure, formulate a theory, then test it. Heisenberg trips us up because, at the most basic level of matter and energy, the act of observing affects the conclusions.

I am willing to accept that at any given moment the universe offers infinite possibilities. We can neither predict nor predictably affect the transitions our lives will make from moment to moment. We can describe our lives as following a pattern of intent. We may work hard toward some precious goal (earn an education, get a job, make great art, publish a book, meet a mate, have children), but we need the universe to cooperate at uncountable critical moments over the seasons and days and seconds to accomplish it. Sometimes it does this in surprising ways, and we call it fate or coincidence, happenstance, kismet, synchronicity, or destiny. If these things turn against us, we may lose everything. We can sustain an injury, miss an opportunity, or learn that we have inherited a chromosomal abnormality. We are constantly working against the inevitable randomness of the universe as if flying into a shifting wind. It is neither with us nor against us, but a constant challenge to realizing our desires.

To make up for her body's reluctance to produce the critical hormone progesterone, Ruby must take injections of it once a day. It comes in clear glass tubes, suspended in oil like cheap tuna. The injection has to be deposited deep into the muscle of her buttocks. Here are some of the side effects of shooting up progesterone: shortness of breath or pain in the chest, numbness or tingling in an arm or leg, prolonged and heavy vaginal bleeding, stomach pain, dizziness, drowsiness, abdominal pain, headache, diarrhea, discharge, mood changes, anxiety, irritability, and depression. Ruby has had all of them, in exactly that order. Still, and stoically, she is reluctant to complain. We entered into this unpleasantness voluntarily. There is no point in crabbing about a self-inflicted wound.

In the evenings before we started IVF, Ruby and I would wait until Ben was asleep, then enjoy some time to ourselves. We might sit together in the living room and read. We might watch television, or creep upstairs to make love. Our new regimen is to lumber into the downstairs bathroom, which we have transformed into a medical laboratory. Ruby pulls a clear, plastic box off the shelf and begins to unload it: compact vials of liquid with arcane labels, multicolored sets of syringes and needles neatly wrapped in plastic, wads of gauze pads seeped in alcohol. Ruby washes her hands, lays the paraphernalia on the bathroom counter, and deftly assembles the formula. We only received brief instructions on how to prepare and administer the shots, and there is so much mixing, drawing up, and changing of needles involved that one practically needs a nursing degree. While Ruby works, I go to the kitchen and set the teapot to boil. After the shot, she will have a cup of tea and some chocolates to take her mind off the discomfort.

I return to the bathroom and collect the syringe. It contains 10cc of a transparent, yellow liquid that looks like apple juice or urine. The needle itself is long enough to pith a goat. Ruby lies prone on the sofa, exposing a hip so bruised and lacerated it looks like she's been in a fight. I poke at her hip to find a place that doesn't smart, then swab at it with an alcohol pad and count to three. (This pause between swipe and jab is excruciating to Ruby, but it allows me to gather my composure, so my hand is steady.) Now. A quick poke and the oh-so-nauseating glide. I shove all two inches into her and squeeze on the piston until the entire dose has been ejaculated, then pull it out quickly and daub the wound with gauze. In a moment, Ruby pulls up her pants and sits on the edge of the sofa, a faint wince still visible on her face.

Here is how Big Science explains what's happening inside Ruby: Each embryonic cell contains twenty-three pairs of chromosomes. A chromosome is a strand of DNA. The DNA molecule, famously shaped like a pair of mating Slinkys ready to flip-flop down a staircase, is a chapter of a book that describes how to build a person. The paragraphs and sentences are made up of a four-word vocabulary of amino acids: adenine (A), cytosine (C), guanine (G), thymine (T). After a cell divides, a special agent called Messenger RNA adheres to the DNA and flits along the inseam, reading the code like Braille. ACT CAG TTT—it's an eye cell; CAA GCG ATC TAG—

it's going to be blue, just like its mother's. The RNA helps turn the code into proteins, more unwieldy strands that fold in and upon and among themselves. Unfolded, a single strand of protein may be as much as a meter long, yet ten thousand of them would fit comfortably within a space as wide as the dot on a ten-point letter *i*. The shape of the protein is critical to its function and is determined partially by atomic forces. Protein interactions in a living being affect every biological function from reproduction, to immune response, to learning. The process of DNA replication and protein folding repeats in every living thing from the moment of conception to the moment of death.

With all this translation and transcription and folding and unfolding going on, things can go awry. And they often do. In a genetic game of "telephone," the information passed from parent to progeny might not arrive at the next generation in its intended form. For example, ATG might be copied as ATC, or entire sequences could be deleted. There are hundreds of reasons for mutations to arise. Not all mutations result in visible anomalies like having extra toes or multicolored eyes. Darwin's theory of evolution is based on the idea that creatures born with genetic mutations in harmony with the environment can live long enough to reproduce. Isn't that easier to accept than author Rudyard Kipling's *Just So* story about a mouse stretching the elephant's nose into a trunk? Cellular mutations occur all through our lives as individuals, too. Witness the aging process, hairy moles, and of course, cancer.

Some evolutionary biologists go so far as to claim the life of the individual, or *soma*, is merely one stage in the life of a family line, or *genotype*. This "genotype creature" will continue to live as long as each generation of soma reproduces, and thus evolutionary adaptation can be seen as a survival mechanism of a longer-lived organism. If the life of the soma is a heartbeat in the life of the genotype, then the reproductive imperative is as critical as breathing. While this point of view challenges our sense that we are distinct individuals with no more to share with our ancestors than blood and stories, it leads us to the conclusion that our lives do not end with our deaths, but continue—not metaphorically or spiritually, but physically, chemically—with the lives of our children and our children's children. The belief that we are constrained to a single life of eighty-odd years as self-contained individuals with a definite beginning and ending is an artifact of our myopic perception of time. If memory were transmitted by DNA, then we would *feel* more like a sixty-million-year-old organism. Instead, every generation is crippled by selective amnesia. The individual might pass her pinkish skin and green eyes to the next generation, who might have a predilection for red wine from her mother and grandmother, but they have no recollection of the crisis that brought their genotype to North America, or, for that matter, where they put the keys before they left the *shtetl*. We are as the story of the Dot and the Line. The Dot perceives the universe as a single point, neither deep nor wide, and has no patience for the Line's ridiculous talk about length. The Line remains smug and content in his two-dimensionality, thinking he knows all there is to know about the universe. Then he meets the Cube.

Perhaps the answer to the paradoxical behavior of waves and particles lies in a new perception of time or space, or both. Some late twentieth-century physicists have proposed that, on an ultra-small scale, objects such as bosons, leptons, and quarks are composed of extremely compact bundles of energy that might exist in as many as twenty-six dimensions, but we cannot explain their behaviors because organic beings have biological limitations that constrain us to perceiving only three. That sounds like a wacky, far-fetched idea, but it is no more ridiculous than the proposition that inheritance is governed by twisty-tie molecules packed inside a cell. Would it be naïve to propose that individual atoms in folded molecules like proteins are bound up so tightly together that their behavior might, in subtle ways, be governed by quantum interactions? We can neither confirm nor deny that this is the case. One can only state that human beings are made of the same stuff as everything else in the universe, and so we are likely to partake of every wonderful thing in it.

Three weeks into this mess, Ruby starts rummaging through the clothes she wore during her pregnancy with Ben. These consist of size large and extra-large skirts and shifts and also, for later on, a few tent-like *shmattes* that give new meaning to the term "triple-X."

"I'm going to start showing soon," she says, "and I'll need something to wear."

I don't have the heart to remind her that the chances are slim. I want a second child, too, but I'm not ready to dress for it. And when Ruby asks, I refuse to set up the baby-changing table again. If the pregnancy fails, I will have to put the stuff back in the basement, or worse, give it all away. Ben makes enough noise to fill our house, but sometimes during his nap, I find myself looking around for his little sibling. I awaken in the middle of the night thinking I hear an infant crying. The embryo growing inside Ruby is both there and not there, both alive and not, and will remain so until our own measurement problem is resolved at the eight-week ultrasound exam. This incipient child's life is a faint chimera. It is carried in and out of the universe on the quality of our thoughts. Enticed by good thoughts, repelled by ambivalence, this embryo hesitantly dips a toe into existence, then re-treats. I do not believe in spirits, but I am not so sure I believe in the incontrovertibility of chemistry and phys-ics, either. After all, twentieth-century science tells us that things are not always as they seem.

The world outside our home has not changed, yet we feel as if everything is different. We go through our days like automatons, packing Ben off to daycare, making ap-propriate sounds on the phone. Information comes into my brain but doesn't sink in. I am elsewhere. I begin to exhibit the kind of dissociative psychopathy common to people in mourning or in mental hospitals, people who are unable to assimilate their personal drama with the mundane indifference of the outside world. Dishes pile up in the sink. Laundry goes undone. One day I arrive at work and realize, too late, that I am wearing the same T-shirt I slept in. My job as a computer programmer suffers. I find myself spending less time writing software and more time surfing websites about fertility, pregnancy, Heisenberg, truth. From my coworkers' perspective, this is the evidence that something big is going on in my life, though I have not said a word. Our project has turned into more than a preoccupation. It has consumed us.

The clinic hosts an infertility support group that meets on Wednesday nights. Our nurses have suggested that we attend, but I reminded them (with irony) that we would have to hire a babysitter. In fact, the thought of sharing our experience with other couples, or worse, having to listen to other couples talk about their issues, is nauseating to both of us. Ruby and I make a point of avoiding public catharsis in any form—group therapy, Internet chat, guided tours—preferring instead to work things out for ourselves through observation or reading. Ruby has a supernatural memory for written material. More than once she has consumed a guidebook about a new city in half an hour, then shown me around the place as if she were a native. In a similar fashion, she has absorbed all of the available lay literature on in-vitro fertilization, embryology, endocrinology, and genetics. For Ruby, there is a direct connection between knowledge and control. She studies these things in order to own them, to exert some mastery over the chemical, physiological processes that have conspired against her to obliterate something she wants dearly. A less intellectual person would punch a wall.

While book knowledge serves us well in following the course of her treatment, it is useless when Ruby is under the influence of her hormone overdoses. The smallest thing—a television commercial, an expired carton of milk—will cause her to crack, sending her into paroxysms of uncontrollable weeping. When she comes up for air, she gulps something rational, like, "It's entirely because of the drop in my estrogen level." This is how it feels to be in two overlapping states. It is a constant struggle to keep rationality and emotions in balance.

Two weeks after the pregnancy test, we begin to see external manifestations of trouble. Ruby is bleeding constantly at a rate that might only be a side effect of the progesterone or might mean that the endometrial lining is breaking down in preparation for miscarriage. Still, there is no proof, either way. Ruby has begun to show signs of giving up. She had started out determined not to become emotionally attached. Now she has begun to make plans for the next round of treatments. This is not the pregnancy we had hoped for. There is no sublime, contented bliss. There is no quiet jubilation. There is only dull, gray uneasiness that descends on our home like a caul. Black and white have disappeared. There are no clearly defined edges, no answers, no punch lines. Only the painful prick and glide of the two-inch needle briefly piercing the shroud.

Ben's fourth birthday is in a week. It is a significant milestone for all of us, for it means that he has transformed from a toddler to a little boy, and the days of diapers, pacifiers, and midnight awakenings are behind us. It also means that Ben's sibling, who we had hoped would arrive by the time Ben turned three, was a year late. We are doing everything we can to shield Ben from the stress of our fertility program. We want him to have a special celebration for this birthday. We decide to take him to a working farm in Vermont where he can pet the animals. The farm is a family-run business that focuses on making children and their parents feel welcome. The owners live in an idyllic white farmhouse on a hill surrounded by a number of outbuildings where the animals dutifully produce milk, eggs, and wool. Every guest room in the converted barn has a separate bedroom for children, so the adults can get some sleep. In the morning, we swipe eggs from under the hens and carry them in wicker baskets to a communal dining hall where our child can watch them be turned into breakfast. We cannot imagine a healthier environment for city folk.

The morning we arrive, there is a commotion in the sheep pen. A lamb had been born just an hour previous, and a pack of families has crowded in to catch sight of the new arrival. A skinny farmhand crouches inside the pen cleaning up the mess. The lamb is barely two feet long and is covered in blood and ectoplasm. Its eyes are barely open, and every so often it lets out a tiny, confused bleat. What am I doing here? Where is my milk? Why are all these people staring at me? I lift up Ben, so he can stand on one of the rails of the pen and look in. He leans inward and trembles with excitement and fascination. Ruby reaches between the rails and tries to touch the lamb, only she cannot reach. She looks up desperately at me, then at the farmhand.

"Can I touch him?" she asks.

"Not right now. But if you come back in a couple of days, I'll let you hold him."

By the end of the day, our son is gamboling down a hillside toward a duck pond, and we are running after him, laughing. Ruby takes my hand as we run—one of those small gestures of intimacy that have been infrequent since we started IVF. In this momentary lapse of anxiety that I mistake for real joy, I can accept the idea that we might not have another child. Three is a fine size for a family. It is compact and manageable. It would be easier to focus all of our attention and resources on the child we have, and he would not have to suffer the trauma of being deposed by a younger sibling. Of course, a thought lasts only an instant. It is immeasurably short, as a point is immeasurably small. A thought like this, mitigated by the prevailing circumstances, has no edge definition, no beginning and end. One cannot be aware of experiencing something so brief. What exists in one's mind is the memory of the thought as soon as it has left you.

That night in the cabin, something wakes me from a deep sleep. It feels as if I had just closed my eyes a moment earlier, but I can tell from the stillness that many hours had passed. Snow is falling, and against the pre-dawn light, the white flakes look gray. The cold reaches in through our inadequate bedding and urgently pinches my naked toes. My body keeps time while I am asleep. I have never used an alarm clock, and I do not wear a watch. With a small amount of concentration, I can get a good night's sleep and awaken refreshed precisely at an hour and minute of my choosing. This is a convenient trick, and it is probably more common than one would think. But I often wonder what is going on inside one's brain that allows a person to accomplish it. Why should a person's biological clock be so accurately synchronized with the mechanical one? Any surface-bound earth creature is born with the same rhythm beating in its body, and while the choice of twelves and sixties is arbitrary, the daily progression and regression of the sun is part of our *gestalt* from the moment we are born. Parents lose a great deal of sleep coercing their newborns to follow the beat of the Sun, and perhaps it is in these earliest days that our internal clocks are tuned. Whether through an inborn trait or a learned habit made more accurate through practice, I knew when I awoke that it was four-thirty in the morning on Ben's birthday.

In this fragile nether-time before dawn, I hear Ben breathing in the little bed in the next room, the short breaths chirping through his nose at roughly two-second intervals. Ruby is not in the bed next to me, where she should be sleeping. A blade of light slips under the bathroom door. I hear noises coming from in there, but they are hard to make out. The crumpling of paper, perhaps, a few sniffles. Then, the unmistakable sound of Ruby crying. I toss the covers off and throw myself out of bed to stand in front of the door.

"Are you okay?" I ask, knocking lightly.

Light rushes into the room when Ruby opens the door. She pulls me into the cramped bathroom, so we will not wake our child. She has a wad of toilet paper in her hand. It is soiled with blood. In the middle, a dark, gelatinous mass that looks like a ball of snot.

"I dropped it on my toe," she says. "I woke up with cramping, then came in here and before I—it just fell out."

My first reaction is to help her find a way to put it back in. This, before my rational brain has a chance to assimilate the situation. I can't say how long I stand there trying to force myself to reason intelligently, like trying to wake oneself from a bad dream, but it feels like the longest continuous period of abject dumbness I have experienced in recent years. "Do you think we should keep it to show the doctor?" I ask. I can't think of a single good reason why, but I can't bear the thought of throwing it down the toilet. She drops it into a paper cup.

"Put it in the cooler. I'll be out in a moment." She gently pushes me out of the bathroom. I hear her weeping quietly behind the door.

For our unborn fetus, at least, this is the way the world ends. Not with a whimper or a bang, but with a premature glide into incandescent light. Our measurement problem has been solved. Schrödinger's box is open, and the cat is dead.

It is August 2005, and *The New York Times* reports that scientists in South Korea have announced the birth of a healthy clone of a dog. They say cloning a dog is harder than with any other mammal because of the dog's peculiar reproductive physiology; a bitch only goes into estrus twice a year, and it is hard to predict when her ovaries will release the eggs. The Koreans tried no fewer than one-hundred-twenty-three times to get their dog pregnant with its own genetic material. The lead scientist, flush from the praise and astonishment of the world's scientific community, appears on the television holding a cute chocolate Labrador puppy. He attributes his accomplishment to brute force and determination applied over many years. The puppy looks perfect. He doesn't know he is a clone. He soaks up the adoration and amazement of his human benefactors as if there were nothing more natural in the world. The scientists may think they know, but in fact they do not have a clue why puppy number one-twenty-three survived, while numbers one through one-twenty-two did not. Neither have we a clue how many times is enough for us. Our success at pregnancy does not come incrementally as it does with practicing the piano or building a bridge. Each attempt is a toss of the dice, and you keep trying until you win.

The next morning, I take Ben to breakfast and let Ruby sleep in late. When we return to the cabin, she is dressed and ready to go. She gives Ben a big hug. "Let's go see that lamb," she says.

As we trudge up the hill toward the barn, I ask her how she feels.

"I'm done," she says.

"Done?"

"Look, I'm a wreck. My body is tired, and I feel run down all the time. I've been high and low like an addict. My butt hurts. I'm tired of being poked and prodded and examined and measured, having blood drawn. I'm tired of getting up at five o'clock and driving to the clinic. I'm tired of the headaches and being cranky. I want to stop thinking about fertility and spend more time with Ben. And now I've had a miscarriage. I'm done. Let's get on with our lives."

We will never know what was growing inside Ruby's uterus. The doctor says it could have been a fetus or just an incipient placenta. He never saw the specimen because the nurses, accustomed to distraught women dropping defunct morsels of biomaterial at their feet like cats do with mice and birds, patted us compassionately and slipped the thing into a bio-waste container while we weren't looking. Ruby chooses to believe it was alive, though I think that makes the loss harder to bear. I choose to believe it never existed, which might make me a pessimist or a coward. In any case, we are relieved that the waiting is over.

The existential perplexity of the previous month has given way to an equally vexing mix of grieving and relief. The world doesn't owe us another child. It didn't owe us the child we have, or the one we lost but never had. We can only be grateful for the stroke that diverted us from bringing something into the light that was more suited to darkness. Let it live in our minds more happy than in flesh, and let us all find peace.

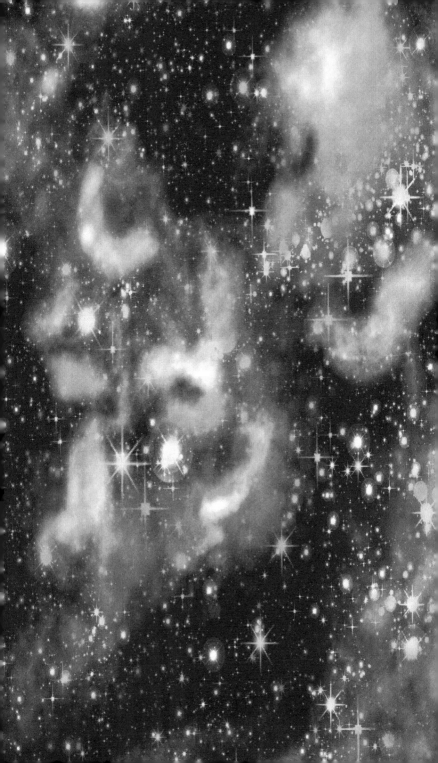

ABOUT THE AUTHOR

Joel Wachman's essays have won awards from Alternating Current Press and *Sycamore Review* and a runner-up place for the Wabash Award. His work has been published in *Harvard Review*, the *Boston Globe*, two anthologies from Universal Table Press, and elsewhere. His father was a scientist and his mother a schoolteacher, so naturally he became a critical thinker who loves literature. After earning a Bachelors in Cognitive Science at Harvard and a Masters at the MIT Media Laboratory, he spent a decade in Paris. There, he published a series of chapbooks, *Par Avion*, which was sold by *bouquinistes* along the Seine. Now working as a computer scientist, Joel builds information systems for a research institute that develops treatments for cancer. He lives in Cambridge, Massachusetts.

ACKNOWLEDGMENTS

These essays were written in the early 2000s while my wife and I were trying to have a second child. I am grateful to Dr. Samuel Pang at Reproductive Sciences of Boston, who facilitated our successful pregnancy and shared his competence and compassion thereafter. My education in quantum physics came from science writers who had the skill to make a mind-bending subject accessible. Brian Greene's *The Elegant Universe* was one such source. Thank you to Michael Litos, formerly of SLAC National Accelerator Laboratory and currently a physics professor and researcher at University of Colorado–Boulder, for finding inaccuracies in my early drafts. He is a real physicist; I am merely an amateur. Thank you, also, to the staff at Alternating Current Press, and in particular to Paige Ferro and Leah Angstman, for their keen eye for detail. Jean Klingler and Michele Markarian, excellent writers with infinite patience, listened to me read these essays aloud more than once, then shared the gift of cold-blooded criticism. This book's title essay won first prize for creative nonfiction from *M Review*, the literary magazine from the now-defunct Marylhurst University. *Requiesce in pace.*

This book is dedicated to my wife, Leslie Shelman, and my son, Sam Wachman. You are the nucleus of my universe.

ENDNOTE

The line from the end of "The Hand of God" comes from William Shakespeare's *The Tempest.*

WORKS CITED

Charles, Dan. 1992. "Fatal explosion closes cold fusion laboratory." *New Scientist*, January 11.

Darwin, Charles. 2003. *On the Origin of Species*. New York: Penguin Random House Signet Classics.

Dawkins, Richard. 1976. *The Selfish Gene*. Oxford, UK: Oxford University Press.

Dillard, Annie. 1988. *A Pilgrim at Tinker Creek*. New York: Harper Colophon.

Greene, Brian. 1999. *The Elegant Universe*. New York: Random House.

Henderson, Mark. 2003. "Artificial sperm signal end to male infertility." *The Times*, December 11.

Howe, Sarah. October 2015. "Relativity (for Stephen Hawking)." *Paris Review* Online.

Lightman, Alan. 1999. *Einstein's Dreams*. New York: Random House.

Lightman, Alan. 2009. *Song of Two Worlds*. Pasadena, CA: Red Hen Press.

Maimonides, Moses. 2000. *A Guide to the Perplexed*. New York: Dover Editions.

McFadden, Johnjoe. 2000. *Quantum Evolution: The New Science of Life*. New York: W. W. Norton & Company.

Milton, John. 1999. *Paradise Lost*. Project Gutenberg.

Saramago, Jose. 1999. *The Stone Raft*. New York: Harcourt Brace.

Schrodinger, Erwin. 1944. *What is Life*. Cambridge, UK: Cambridge University Press.

COLOPHON

The edition you are holding is the First Edition of this publication.

The cursive text is set in Amylight, created by Olex Studio. The block text is set in Lemon Milk, created by Marsnev™. The san serif text is set in Avenir Book, created by Adrian Frutiger. All other text is set in Athelas, created by Jose Scaglione and Veronika Burian. The Alternating Current Press logo is set in Portmanteau, created by JLH Fonts. All fonts used with permission; all rights reserved.

Other Works from

ALTERNATING CURRENT PRESS

alternatingcurrentarts.com

Made in the USA
Middletown, DE
17 November 2021

52023381R00087